My Soul in Exile

and Other Writings

ZABEL YESSAYAN

My Soul in Exile

and Other Writings

Edited by Barbara Merguerian

With Joy Renjilian-Burgy, Judith A. Saryan, and Danila Jebejian Terpanjian

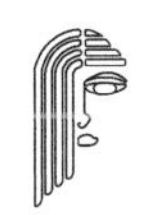

AIWA PRESS
Armenian International Women's Association
Boston, Massachusetts

This publication was made possible

by a generous grant from

the Dolores Zohrab Liebmann Fund

Cover Design: Taline Boghosian
Cover Painting: "Sea View by Moonlight"(1878) by Ivan Aivazovsky © 2014, State Russian Museum, St. Petersburg
Graphic Design: Mark McKertich

Armenian International Women's Association, Inc.
65 Main St., #3A, Watertown, MA 02472
www.aiwainternational.org

ISBN: 978-0-9648787-7-8
Library of Congress Control Number: 2013956756

Printed in the United States of America

Contents

TRANSLATORS FOR THIS VOLUME

G. M. Goshgarian *(My Soul in Exile,* "In the Ruins") was educated at Yale and UCLA and has translated twenty books and many shorter works from German, French, and Armenian into English. Most recently his English translation of part of the Armenian author Hagop Oshagan's epic novel *Remnants* has been published by Gomidas Press. He is the author of a book on nineteenth-century American popular literature, *To Kiss the Chastening Rod* (Cornell University Press, 1992). His edition of the French Marxist philosopher Louis Althusser's *Initiation à la philosophie pour non-philosophes* (Paris, Presses universitaires de France) is in press.

Jennifer Manoukian (several "Early Works" and "Essays") is a translator, lecturer, and literary critic. Her scholarly research examines issues of cultural identity in Western Armenian literature. In addition to her translation of Zabel Yessayan's memoir, *The Gardens of Silihdar,* Manoukian has published critical articles on Yessayan's other works of fiction and nonfiction. A major in French literature and Middle Eastern studies, she is a graduate of Rutgers University.

Nanore Barsoumian ("Newest Manifestations of the Women's Cause") is assistant editor of the *Armenian Weekly,* where her writings focus on human rights, politics, poverty, and environmental and gender issues. She is a graduate of the University of Massachusetts (Boston) with a degree in Political Science and English.

Brief Biography of Zabel Yessayan

In the creative outburst that marked the Armenian renaissance of the late nineteenth and early twentieth centuries, women played an active role. The victory of the vernacular Western Armenian language in the struggle over classical texts resulted in the rapid growth of schools, periodicals, publishing houses, and social organizations of many kinds. Among the many facets of this renaissance was an emphasis on educating women and advancing their position in society. Educated women began writing and editing articles and books, entering teaching as a profession, and establishing humanitarian organizations.

It was during this vibrant period of Armenian culture that the writer and activist Zabel Yessayan established a reputation as a prominent Armenian intellectual. Her turbulent life, reflected in her writing, followed the vicissitudes of the Western Armenians of the period. Born Zabel Hovhannessian in Constantinople (Istanbul) in 1878, Yessayan graduated from the Armenian Holy Cross secondary school, where she had excelled in her studies, especially literature. Her first works were published in 1895, the same year that she left for Paris and enrolled in the Sorbonne, thus becoming one of the first Ottoman women to study abroad.

In Paris she married the painter Dikran Yessayan, with whom she had two children, Sophie and Hrant. Her first novel, *The Waiting Room,* published in 1903, takes place in Paris and explores themes that were to become central to her work—exile and alienation.

Returning to Constantinople in 1902, she began writing articles about contemporary issues; these appeared in various Armenian and French publications. In 1909 she was appointed to a delegation sent to Adana to provide aid to orphans and assess conditions in the aftermath of the bloody massacres of the Armenians that had taken place a few months earlier. Her classic account of this experience, published as *In the Ruins,* is widely regarded as one of her best works.

The only woman on the "black list" of the Armenian intellectuals to be arrested on the night of April 24, 1915, Yessayan was able to elude the police, and after spending several months in hiding managed to escape to Bulgaria. There she found only temporary refuge and was forced to flee again when Bulgaria entered the war as an ally of Ottoman Turkey. The following years found her busy at work in the Caucasus, writing and publishing interviews with survivors of the Armenian Genocide and also organizing the care and relocation of refugees and orphans. By 1922 she returned to Paris and resumed her writing, publishing the psychological novels *My Soul in Exile* in that year, followed by *Hours of Agony* and *The Last Cup.*

In the 1920s Yessayan visited Soviet Armenia, and in 1933 accepted an invitation to move there and teach literature at Yerevan State University. At the same time she continued her writing with the novel *Shirt of Fire* (1934) and *The Gardens of Silihdar* (1935). After years of wandering, it seemed that she had found a permanent, safe home. But this stable life was not to last. In the face of increasing criticism of creative artists by Communist government officials, Yessayan staunchly defended the works of such talented writers as Aksel Bakunts and Yeghishe Charents. Becoming along with them a victim of Stalin's purges of Armenian intellectuals, she was arrested in 1937, imprisoned and tortured in exile in Baku, and died under unknown circumstances, probably in 1943. Left unwritten were several plays and projects, including a biographical novel based on the life of the poet Bedros Turian, the second and third volumes of her memoir *The Gardens of Silihdar,* and a major novel titled "The Dream of Shahabed."

Preface

Almost forgotten today, Zabel Yessayan is the subject of a documentary film, *Finding Zabel Yesayan,* prepared in 2011 by Talin Suciyan and Lara Aharonian and widely shown in the Armenian diaspora. Inspired by the presentation of the film in the Boston area, a group of women, members of the Armenian International Women's Association (AIWA), began to develop a plan to translate into English and publish some of Yessayan's works. The first task, to choose the works to be published, became a challenge when we realized the vast output of her novels, short stories, poetry, and articles on many subjects published across a span of decades in publications appearing throughout Armenia and the Armenian diaspora, many of them difficult to locate today.

After much thought and discussion, it was decided to publish two volumes, one—the companion to this book—containing the complete text of *The Gardens of Silihdar,* Yessayan's thinly veiled memoir of her early years growing up in Constantinople, a work that has been available in English up to this time only in an out-of-print abridged edition translated and edited by Ara Baliozian.

This volume contains Yessayan's short but revealing novel, *My Soul in Exile,* published in 1922 in Vienna by the Mekhitarist Press. Yessayan's first major work written after the Armenian Genocide, the novel is set in Constantinople during the critical period following the 1909 Adana massacres and preceding the 1914 outbreak of World War I. The complete text is followed by an analysis of this many-layered novel by the literary critic Krikor Beledian. Also included in this volume are selections of Yessayan's early works, some of her articles dealing with contemporary issues, and a brief reminiscence by one of her students at Yerevan State University, Ruben Zaryan. We hope that these selections will provide the reader with a useful introduction to the life and accomplishments of this remarkable author.

Thanks are due to many individuals who have contributed in various ways to this publication, especially the translators (chiefly Jennifer Manoukian and G. M. Goshgarian), who provided an English text as close as possible to the Armenian original. Lara Aharonian of the Women's Resource Center in Yerevan helped to obtain material from the Museum of Literature and Art in Armenia. Many pleasant and stimulating hours were spent with co-editors Joy Renjilian-Burgy, Judith A. Saryan, Danila Jebejian Terpanjian, and occasionally others, as we searched to find material, shape the publications, and especially as we steeped ourselves into the life and works of this talented author. Special appreciation is due to Victoria Rowe, whose groundbreaking study, *A History of Armenian Women's Writing, 1880-1922,* has done much to attract attention to the pioneering authors of the period.

We are grateful to the Dolores Zohrab Liebmann Fund, for a generous publication grant, and to the Board of Directors of the Armenian International Women's Association, for their constant support.

This is one in a series of English-language translations published by AIWA and devoted to the works of Armenian women writers and editors of the late nineteenth and early twentieth centuries. There is a rich treasury available, waiting to be tapped, important for those interested in the role of women in the late Ottoman Empire and in the far-reaching effects of World War I. More broadly, while dated in some respects, the literature of this period has surprising relevance to current issues, not only those surrounding the position of women in society, but also to larger questions such as ethnic identity, alienation, and social justice. If our modest volumes serve to inspire others to delve more deeply into the lives and writings of Zabel Yessayan and her contemporaries, then our hopes will have been realized.

—*Barbara Merguerian*

My Soul in Exile

I returned to Constantinople today. It is spring, and the April night with its sultry, fragrant atmosphere fills me with sweet emotion. Standing in my father's nearly deserted house in Bağlarbaşi at the open window all alone, I have been lost in thought for a long time. But I am not really thinking, of course; nor am I dreaming. Rather, abandoning my soul to a fleeting, undefinable emotion, I silently steep myself in the beauty of nature and, by degrees, enter into communion with it.

It is neither night nor day. A starry white, iridescent tremolo of light makes everything vacillate, even the profile of the mountain range in the distance. Quivering streaks of light incessantly flame up and then melt away in the valley in which the soil, agitated by the labor of its fecundation, exhales a humid, heady fragrance. Waves of balmy wind ripple through the air, but they do not gradually mix with the coolness of the evening and temper it. That, no doubt, is why the sudden buffets of cold make me shiver, despite the feverish heat searing my forehead.

A newly bloomed flower perfumes the air, a shooting star traces its luminous furrow across the sky, and frogs croak in the pools of the vegetable gardens: a protracted, stubborn, monotonous sound. How penetrating, moving, and deep that eternal song of the frogs is! It reminds me of other springs and, with surprising force, arouses a sad homesickness in me. . . . All I want now is to lie down, rest, and think about everything I have to do tomorrow; but I am glued to the spot by those humble animals' lovesick spring song. It is as if I were still far from Constantinople and my father's house in Scutari; it is as if I were only remembering that croaking, as if a tender emotion were disarming my soul.

In the recesses of my memory, closed doors are opening and past moments are reawakening. A word, a forgotten gesture, a look of my father's, or even details of everyday existence long since past and forgotten, are coming back to life. I do not remember them so much as they once again communicate to me the sorrow or joy they contain.

A long, very long series of notes of the same pitch, seemingly emitted with breathless haste, melts into another series, louder or softer, and so on without end . . . without end. I must nevertheless shut the window and rest. Tomorrow I will have to spend the entire day in the customhouse trying to wrest my paintings from the customs officers' grip.

That dread operation was accomplished with an ease I had not at all been expecting; no questions were asked and everything was returned to me. Constitutional Turkey[1] has a particularly friendly, warm attitude toward us. This is a country that confronts you with utterly unpredictable situations. It seems there is no transition between one state of affairs and the next: things are either very good or very bad.

I've already hung my pictures on the walls of the big room, covered with Ottoman-style murals painted by my talented grandfather. The artfulness of those arabesques is now hidden beneath the serried frames of my paintings. I spend entire days penned up in that room. Sometimes I regard my work with the critic's severe eye, now despondently, at other times with admiration. I would have liked to produce something else, and surely there was something else in my soul. Inside me was light, gaiety, and life, yet all my paintings are shrouded in mist. My native land's luminous sun has yet to rise in my work, but I feel certain that the mist will be dispelled in future works and that my day will dawn.

It is difficult to explain the train of thought that has brought me to this conclusion. It is as if my yearning and longing for a homeland were themselves that mist and that sadness, as if they have set their seal on my character as well. I have been searching for myself interminably and have suffered deeply in the process, and that wrenching spiritual effort has left its mark on my work.

Will I ever be understood? Or simply, will anyone ever appear who can appreciate or assess my work at its true value? Will people understand this much at least: that my defects do not stem from carelessness or chance, but are, rather, the consequence of a certain irrepressible inclination?

This morning, when the sun rose brightly, flooding everything in its light, my paintings seemed pale and devoid of the emotion that, in my friends' estimation, communicates itself so easily to others. In the pinkish evening mist, however, they seemed to be of value again, and I remained sitting in front of them for a long time, thinking and dreaming. I felt relieved then; I begin to look at my work confidently and even, gradually, to admire it. This evening my soul is in accord with the states of mind that gave birth to those pictures. I am, perhaps, adding my particular mood to their real merits, filling them out in my imagination, making good their defects, and gradually I begin to feel excited.

I nevertheless sense that, in a certain way, I have not yet found a way of expressing myself forthrightly. Perhaps my palette should have been different. I should perhaps have looked for another way of apprehending my subject. No, no! There's no point in wandering down those blind alleys again. . . .

The fact of the matter is that this genre doesn't correspond to my inner inclination. I'm not really a painter. My teacher characterized me accurately, putting his finger on the sore spot when he said, "You, Madam, create music with colors and lines."

"You couldn't have hoped for higher praise," my friends told me.

From a certain standpoint, that's true. To transcend the boundaries of one art and cross over into the domain of another is the kind of feat that always amazes people, and amazement is the better part of admiration. But I don't want to approach this problem in terms of success or failure.

At this very moment, I'm invaded by doubt again. I want to examine myself and come to know my turbulent inner world.

It's true that inspiration comes to me not visually, but as music. It's a kind of mute, intimate, profoundly mysterious symphony that whispers and then thunders in my soul. It doesn't sound like any known musical instrument or human voice. It has the broad, serene rhythm of the sea, of the wind or the woods, and sometimes of a murmuring brook. Where does this inner harmony come from? What is its source? What external causes are capable of bringing it into being? I cannot clearly say.

It seems that the connections between the outside world and my inner self are often broken or become imperceptible to me, and that I draw my inspiration from the depths of my soul, as if from an unhoped-for, unknown treasure-trove. But how different is what I see with my soul's eyes from what I put before the public eye! I seem to thrust my hand, in the dark, into a bag bursting with gold, to hold the treasure tightly in my grip, and cautiously withdrawing my hand, to sense, physically, that the gold is really there—yet, when I open my hand in the broad light of day, nothing is left in it, so that I have to examine it attentively to find the merest trace of gold dust in the imperceptible pores of my skin. There, that's the right comparison.

Thus I have not yet succeeded in expressing or capturing on canvas my soul's music, my inner storms and moments of peace. Will I ever succeed in lifting a corner of the mysterious veil? Will I ever succeed in plunging to the very bottom of my inner depths and reemerging, triumphantly, with clear-eyed consciousness?

I am curious about myself. At any rate, I can say with certainty that what people see in my works is that veil itself, not what lies behind it. It is the very mist that encumbers my soul and makes me a stranger to myself. It is the very sadness that arises from my yearning, my desire, my inadequacy.

I can also say with certainty that I have not succeeded in making music with painting; my brush has, unconsciously perhaps, followed my inner rhythm. My songs and my soul's symphony have remained mute; not a single note of that music has yet sounded. My pictures correspond to the periods of my soul's silence, as if a dancing band of spirits had traversed my inner world and moved on, and everything had turned to stone in their absence. Those are the kind of days when one feels empty and busies oneself by summoning memories to fill the void.

Thus my paintings reflect recollected emotions and are born of such periods of silence. That is why they are lifeless without me: I give them breath, I infuse them with warmth, and only my eyes can appreciate them, because only I know the value of the sadness or serenity they contain.

What can others see in all this? A vague emotion or simply the physical subject of the painting—that is, its more or less pleasing skeleton.

Yet this vague emotion is that surplus, that absolute, which artists consider to be their greatest success. It is my ambition, however, to want still more. Inside me is the effervescence of a wonderful expectation: I feel that my soul is in exile and eagerly awaiting its emancipation. What and who will loosen its chains? At every moment, one can feel hope or despair.

But when that moment comes and my soul knows that exultation, I want to pull a jet of flame from that crackling fire, a fountain of beauty and emotion from that raging storm. At the sight of that miraculous revelation, people can, I know, writhe in agony or joy.

Walking back and forth in front of my paintings the whole day long, thinking, dreaming, and deeply moved, I had become so weak that I was feverish that evening. This fever is my constant companion; it is, perhaps, a consequence of my overwrought state of mind. One of my friends, a kindly, gentle old artist, often used to tell me, quite rightly: "You think too much and that's not good. Surrender to your instincts, the artist's best guide. Be as naive as a child, rediscover the miraculous capacity for amazement and wonder you had in your youngest years. When you do, an insignificant pebble skipping down the road will become a fairy tale for you; the world will be inhabited by spirits, miracles, and wonders; and you will be able to weep or smile. People incapable of seeing those miracles with their own eyes will weep or smile with you. There you have it: that's what art is."

That, perhaps, is the truth, I've often told myself—that I should surrender to my instincts. Yet there are people who have irrevocably lost their childhood because they have heard the announcement of their destiny in the secret depths of their being. How can you smile or gently weep when you feel your fettered soul's wings beating against an invisible threshold?

It must also be said that I have long since turned my back on the easy success that comes by chance. I don't want to be beholden to blind accident for anything. When my brush isn't conducted by my will and my will alone, and produces a harmonious combination of colors or a felicitous outline by accident, I immediately wipe those colors or lines off the canvas.

❧

This is brain fever, but it is also Constantinople fever, a sort of physical agitation inseparable from the city's spring nights. There are so many stirring scents in the air, so much humidity, and at the same time the balmy waves of the southerly wind, and above all, that unstable, constantly shifting, intense emotion that resembles endless death and rebirth. Lights flicker and go out, while an imperceptible murmur, a sort of trembling in the atmosphere, agitates the air and sometimes makes it stifling. It seems as if, from time to time, an invisible bird flies by: the lights are snuffed out by its shadow, and the whispering of the trees ceases. Everything becomes a dream, wild emotion, or nightmare. People roam through the streets, staggering as if drunk. Everything—the natural scene, human emotion, the urban skyline, the soaring poplars, the muezzin's call—everything is not only carried to a feverish pitch of excitement, but also mingles with everything else. I remember that, from a very early age, I felt all this, vaguely: curled up in my bed under rose-scented sheets, I would pull the comforter all the way up to my feverish forehead and shiver, just as I am shivering tonight.

In no other city in the world, perhaps, does the unrest of spring invade people's inner being in this supremely subtle, unhealthy way.

❧

At sundown, seated at my desk, I was leafing through a pile of newspapers. I was reading with amusement the empty flattery written about me when Sebuhian came calling with an old teacher of mine, Hrant Cherkezian. Hardly had Sebuhian greeted me than, throwing the shock of hair that had fallen over his forehead back with a toss of his head, he fastened his eyes on the papers and said, laughing out loud: "What nincompoops!"

Hrant Cherkezian has aged; yet in spite of his salt-and-pepper beard and bald head, his face has retained the spirited expression of his youth. He fixes his extremely near-sighted eyes on me, tries to straighten up his bowed back, and clasping my hand firmly in his, says affectionately, "Emma, you've realized all my hopes."

I feel as happy and contented as a child on hearing his words, just as I used to back in the days when I was his favorite pupil. I still distinctly remember the classroom in our neighborhood Armenian school one very hot early summer morning. Countless ladybugs were buzzing behind the windows screened by Venetian blinds. The one tree in the garden, a big linden, was sending its scented breath our way. The teacher was reading us a passage in Classical Armenian. I remember how much the flawless beauty of his reading, the clear, solid structure of the sentences, the lilt of his voice, and the rhythm with which he read moved me, like music, running through my imagination like a series of sculpted forms. I failed to understand much of the passage, and the sense of many of the words escaped me. But, more than their literal meaning, it was our forefathers' spirit that seemed to stand before me. Holding my breath, concentrating, carried away, I surrendered to my dream.

It seemed that a broken bond was about to be renewed; it seemed that my soul was about to return from its exile, shivering with pleasure at recognizing itself. I was on the threshold of unattainable bliss when I suddenly had a rude awakening.

Sebuhian checked my mind's flight into memories of the past. "We've come to take a look at your paintings," he said.

"Gladly," I replied, "but rest for a moment first."

Both of them sat down on a divan running the length of the room. They turned their eyes toward the splendor of the natural scene and gazed for a long time in silent admiration.

The beautiful verdant valley stretches as far as Çamlıca and the lovely undulations of Kayışdağı. That quarter of the city is adorned with pink mist in the morning and purple mist at dusk; at this time of day it has taken on its clearest, most luminous blue and seems to be a pure distillation of the sky. Beyond lies the sea, the marvelous Sea of Marmara with its islands, their hills a prolongation of Kayışdağı's wavelike contours. In the soft evening light, their outline dissolves on the sea's shining bosom, and they take on a dreamy, ethereal character.

Abruptly, Sebouhian turned to me and, his head propped on a pillow, starts talking. "So, then, Madam, you've come back to your country. You did well to return; here you have beautiful scenery and plenty of things to paint, and our community can use fresh talents."

I was startled by his words. What do they expect of me . . . ? Sebuhian is one of those people who go on about art without ever having thought about it. Our joy and sorrow, our religion, mad passion, and incurable illness are, for people of that sort, just a means to an end, worthwhile only when they directly and immediately serve one or the other of the parties locked in struggle.

While thinking about all this, I look more attentively at Sebuhian. His cheerful face and the clear light in his beautiful eyes can suggest the presence of something more than is actually there. But a romantic patriotism blows like an unloosed wind through his inner world, where everything—ideas, feelings, or thoughts—takes on the wild, disoriented turbulence of leaves driven high up into the air by a storm. Despite his rhetorical gifts, he himself doesn't know what he's talking about: the brilliant sentence he utters by accident determines what he goes on to say. His mind resembles a ship with unfurled sails and no helm. He gives an outside observer the impression that he is advancing on a swift, beautiful course toward his goal;

yet he himself doesn't know on what shores he will land, nor even that he can founder on the rocks.

At the day-to-day level, he is, nonetheless, a pleasant fellow, outgoing and well-meaning. I love his smile, which has a grace all its own. It opens like a flower that blooms without effort in the earliest morning sunbeams.

Hrant Cherkezian has aged, but that initial impression once past, I gradually discover traces of the man who had so profound an influence on my childhood and even after, when I learned the story of his tragic life. By ordinary standards, he might be considered ugly. I, however, detect a mysterious, singular beauty in that wrinkled countenance that wears an expression attesting concentrated thought and force of character. His unkempt salt-and-pepper beard covers his cheeks, while his thick lips create an impression of boundless kindness, spiritual kindness. Yet he is not kind in the ordinary sense of the word; his is not the sort of emotional, sentimental kindness triggered only by immediate, superficial impressions or nervous agitation. Indeed, when I tell people that Hrant Cherkezian is kind, they think I'm joking. He carefully hides his noble, tormented feelings of judicious kindness, which embarrass him. It is, perhaps, the better to hide such feelings that he can sometimes be extremely intolerant.

His black eyes, hidden by his glasses, might be considered beautiful. His pockmarked nose, broad forehead, and thinning hair complete this original portrait; they form a whole in which I have always detected a touch of a certain kind of inspiration as well as the deep thoughtfulness of an intellectual of the first rank. That, precisely, is what graces him with eternal youth. He has a slight stoop, but that, too, would appear to be a consequence of his thoughtfulness. It is a sign of strained self-control. His shoulders, too, carry the weight of the strict principles he has imposed on himself.

That man is not only unsettled by his virtues, but unsettles others as well, for the people of our day have carved out a comfortable niche of dubious ethics for themselves, made to measure, and see enemies in those who bear with the discomfort caused them by their own demanding souls. A great many people cannot stand Hrant Cherkezian's uncompromising character. He hardly ever smiles, not because there is no joy in his soul, but because everything in him is buried very deep down. Everything takes place behind that stern, unforgiving mask; what transpires in his soul never breaks to the surface. To know and love him, one has to penetrate the surface and reach his hermetically sealed inner life; and, to do that, one has to discover the path to his heart. The result is of course worth the effort, and I have always wanted to make that discovery. I've often considered painting his portrait: setting out from his apparent ugliness—indeed, thanks precisely to that ugliness—one can depict his spiritual beauty, steeping his portrait in its light.

Just when Sebuhian and Cherkezian were about to step into the big room to look at my paintings, other acquaintances of mine came to visit. Talk immediately turned to the counter-revolutionary movement, the massacres in Cilicia, and the pact in the offing between Turks and Armenians.[2] The conversation rapidly became a dispute, and because people had passionate views on the subject, the noisy debate led everyone to forget all restraint.

What place was there for painting or art in this hell? Night fell and my guests left, arguing all the way to the door. They had completely forgotten why they had come to see me.

It is hard, when passions are so inflamed, when political questions have become decisive and take precedence over everything else, when people live for the day without looking back or fixing their eyes on the horizon of the future—it is hard not just to bring people to take an interest in art, but even to get them to concentrate and give themselves over to our dream with undivided pleasure. When I encounter writers, poets, or musicians who take an active part in the public debates of the day or even put their prestige in this or that party's service, lending it the authority of their names, it seems to me either that they have abandoned their proper role or that I am a useless personage among them, an anomaly with respect to a general, inescapable mentality that one has to bear up under, to tolerate, with infinite patience. It also seems to me that, all immediate concerns notwithstanding, we all have recesses in our souls in which we can always take refuge, inaccessible, authentic sanctuaries that we all build for ourselves. Woe to those whose souls are empty.

The din of the outside world and its cries of pain or joy disturb us, of course, assailing our inner being; but can they extinguish the luminous smile that spread over my face when, coming back on the evening steamboat, I saw the miraculous sunset? What a wealth of hues, what a majestic display of light and color! Gradually, in the violet atmosphere, Constantinople's skyline thickened and grew dark, while a golden ribbon fringed the periphery of the domes and minarets: gold and black lines and nothing else, and then all the colors faded and the sea's surface itself darkened, the crests of its rippling waves glittering with golden sparks.

I often hear the stupid remark, "How many things you have to paint!" Can I reply that my impressions are so overwhelming that I can paint nothing at all at present? Before that dizzying, infinite beauty, I have become a giddy child; it is as if I no longer had the artist's most elementary means at my disposal. One must wait to be imbued with that beauty and all the emotions bestowed on us by our individual and collective existence. One must wait for the soul to be fecundated and, in its inviolable secret, conceive the work that will one day be born. Premature production, impatience, heeding one's first impressions is not creation, but artistic distraction. Only tranquil patience allows me to hope that one day I shall at last succeed in capturing on canvas the imperishable beauty that has already taken form in my soul.

"But you also mustn't miss the moment when success comes knocking," a voice inside me whispers.

That is the whole secret. One must not be overhasty, but one must also not wait too long, so as to wrest from the dull march of time the moment, the creative moment, that holds all our fortune and our glory.

Unexpectedly, I made the acquaintance of Mrs. Siranush Danielian. I had heard a great deal about her, and her book of poems had once been my bedtime reading. Her solid literary reputation and the warm, enthusiastic affection that her friends and acquain. tances showed her made her one of the most influential women in Constantinople. She hasn't written much and her poems appear only rarely, but whenever they do, they have a special, very personal touch. There can be no doubt that she has much more in her than she has expressed; it may even be that, unbeknown to her, she has songs of a different kind in her which, because she will never sing them, will remain forever shrouded in her silence.

I have often thought about her from a distance and have long been curious about her, yet have always shied away from asking for the least information or opinion about her for fear that the physical and moral image of her that I have constructed in my mind might somehow be tarnished.

I first heard her name from Hrant Cherkezian and was deeply

impressed by my teacher's passionate regard for the poet, who at the time was shining like a new star in our literary galaxy. When, later, sure of Cherkezian's opinion, I wanted to discuss Mrs. Danielian's book with him, he interrupted me almost rudely to say that she was worth more than her book was.

What was the reason for Cherkezian's initial enthusiasm and ultimate dissatisfaction? What had disappointed him? At the time it was beyond my comprehension; later, however, I understood Cherkezian. How often, when I was fatigued by my own pursuit of the elusive, unattainable goal, has my soul been soothed by the fresh enthusiasm born of my belief in some other, new talent? What has proven impossible for me and thousands upon thousands like me can prove possible for someone else; a newly revealed talent always has a magic wand in hand and gives us the right to expect a miracle.

Cherkezian had of course seen in Mrs. Danielian's beautiful debut the possibility that one of his aesthetic goals might be fulfilled. That explains his disappointment.

I was waiting on the landing in Scutari with Cherkezian when my teacher whispered in my ear, "Mrs. Danielian!" Of average height, thin, her profile veiled in the shadow cast by a plain, broad-brimmed hat, she was standing a few steps away, waiting for a coach, like us.

"How old is Mrs. Danielian?" I'd been hearing her name for a very long time, and now I was looking in amazement at the woman, with her youthful appearance. Cherkezian approached her. A pair of placid, smiling eyes suddenly turned in my direction and observed me with singular interest. Almost immediately, Cherkezian walked over and introduced me: "Emma, the well-known painter."

An expression of tender gravity came over Mrs. Danielian's face. She held out her hand. I shook it with great pleasure, as if we were old friends.

After we had finally found seats in a coach and started to go up the slope, our glances crossed again. I observed her more intensely. I was already discovering a different figure; the poet's moral physiognomy now appeared in a truer light, with more sharply defined features. Over her smooth forehead, a few white threads embellish her dark brown hair. One cannot say that she has preserved her physical youthfulness, but the expression on her face is illuminated by the radiance of her smile and countenance, and her features are steeped in the freshness of enthusiasm and fervor. One cannot say that she is beautiful and one cannot say that she is ugly, because even the irregularity of her traits is transformed into a peculiar grace by the unusual luminosity of her smile and look, and all this gives rise to a feeling that is in the highest measure infectious. But in her that feeling is a peaceful, permanent psychological state, and as soon as I heard her gentle, calm, poised voice, I was completely subjugated by a feeling of absolute serenity.

We didn't talk much on the way; the jolting coach and the other passengers' curiosity disturbed us.

"I've heard about you and was glad to learn of your successes abroad. I'd like to come see your paintings."

"Oh, Mrs. Danielian," I answered, "I didn't dare invite you to come."

"But why?" she exclaimed, surprised. She briefly fastened her smiling, almost mockingly shining eyes on Cherkezian, who stubbornly continued to say absolutely nothing at all. Then she added, seriously: "There are so few people in this city capable of understanding one another. . . . I hope we'll become good friends."

I wanted to say many things in reply, but I don't know what I stammered. My heart was overflowing with gratitude.

"That's how it is, you know?" she went on. "It's as if we were exiles in a remote foreign country. We're exiles in the land of our birth because we're deprived of the kind of environment that our people's collective existence would create around us. Only fragile, loose threads bind us to our native land." Pensive for a moment, she looked at Cherkezian's frowning face, but then, as if she had suddenly gotten a hold on herself, she continued:

"But we artists, at least, can become comrades in exile." She made these last remarks without sorrow, as if she had already resigned herself to the sad implications of that condition.

An emotion made up of a confused medley of thoughts and feelings arose in me. I wanted to say a thousand different things, but my voice seemed stuck in my throat. No! I have not resigned myself to that sadness: neither the despair of someone like Cherkezian, paralyzed by a fixed idea, nor Mrs. Danielian's sagacious serenity shall ever appear on my face. Nor shall I ever indulge in the dubious pleasure associated with the kind of feelings that drape a young woman's face in an insouciant smile. I shall pursue my dream down every road, and my soul shall have its freedom. I want to inspire everyone with my hope and faith, disseminating them with an open hand everywhere. I want to say: let us become, not "comrades in exile," but "comrades in struggle," seeking pure, authentic sources of inspiration together. But then my exalted gaze alights on Mrs. Danielian's mocking countenance. In the glowing red atmosphere of sundown, hers is so entirely the look of someone resigned to everything. . . . Her delicate profile has acquired a strange transparency and the clear light of her eyes resembles a sun that dawns over a bottomless abyss.

And I, who would have considered myself so different from her—in temperament, character, tastes—suddenly felt not just similar to her, but the same, as if we were two soul sisters: companions in exile.

That, perhaps, is the reason of reasons. Each one of us is alone and, in the best of cases, cuts across foreign skies like a shooting star. However bright, however radiant the trace of light we leave behind, it is doomed to grow dim and disappear. Our individual voices will never blend into the harmony of a chorus. We feel the void beneath our ribs, and surely that is why our soul is shackled by the fetters of our individual sorrow and happiness. Every time that, made restless by its bondage, it starts to beat its wings, its flight is thwarted by the high walls that enclose our individual lives. Only the stormy sea and the unbounded horizon of a collective existence could grace us with the powerful breath of creativity. Driven in upon ourselves, we have no choice but to become as hard as crystal, torn from the past and fenced off from the future.

A soiree at the Varvarians'. The drawing-room windows open onto a garden. It boasts a pair of stately cedars, centuries old; their spreading, umbrella-like branches all but obscure the horizon. Farther off are other gardens and fields, full of wild flowers. In this evening hour, when the flaming firmament grows pale behind the cedars' dense, somber silhouette, a heady scent of wild flowers and sun-burnt soil gradually wafts toward us and, as it were, steeps us in nature's emotion.

Miss Sophie Varvarian is suffering from a bout of incurable melancholy. Who would ever have thought it? Her ironic witticisms and feverish gaiety sustain the prevailing belief that the shadow of sadness never flits across her soul. She is popular and surrounded by admirers, thanks to the ravishing beauty that she wears on her proud face like a mark of glory. One might suppose that she is happy and has attained her every goal.

Tonight, however, she reveals her true countenance to me. I observe her with a painter's analytical eye. Her thick eyebrows, with their flawless arch, lend a haughty expression to her thin, dainty face, which seems somewhat drawn under the impact of intense inner feelings. But what dominates her face and her entire person are her unusually beautiful eyes, overflowing with intelligence.

"Have you ever thought about the fact, Emma, that someday, on some unknown date, at some unknown hour, they're going to put us in a coffin, pale and unfeeling, our hands crossed on our breasts and our shrouds covered with flowers? With flowers, Emma! So that the more or less indifferent people crowding round us can't smell the odors coming from our putrefying bodies."

"Yes, I've thought about that, Emma, often. But, at the same time, I think that it's hard to think about death amid the brightness of light and hope: death is meaningless for us for as long as we're bursting with life and spirit. We can't believe in death now, and that makes it unreal; but later, when the lights gradually dim and our appetites and desires decline, when we start to get old . . ."

"Don't talk about old age. I prefer to die in the full flush of my youth and beauty. I want people's memory of me to remain unblemished; I want to vanish from the face of the earth undiminished, just the way I am now."

"Ah, but a month after we die, however young and beautiful we might have been, we'll look just like the people who've been dead a hundred years."

The fragrance of the distant fields reached us, denser now. The balmy northern wind rippled past, and the cedars rustled for a long time. The horizon was darkening, the last of its colors fading away. White wisps of clouds raced across the sky, as if pursuing a goal. The fragrance of the wisteria in the nearby garden reached us, stronger than it had been, and spread through the air until it dominated the atmosphere. Its increasingly intoxicating waves seemed to be telling us about something indefinable and inexpressible that we nevertheless intuitively understood.

We promptly shut the windows, shivering with the cool of the May evening and perhaps also with the emotion that our strange conversation had instilled in our souls.

Hardly had the thick woolen curtains been drawn and the lamp lit than our dark thoughts vanished and we embarked on a confidential chat. Seated in deep, comfortable armchairs, we abandoned ourselves to the pleasantly warm atmosphere, which was saturated with the aroma of incense; we felt singularly at ease and safe from all evil, and our thoughts blossomed, bright and bold, sometimes strange and sometimes even freakish, like greenhouse flowers.

We ate our meal in high spirits. On our way back to the drawing-room, I asked Sophie, "And Mrs. Danielian?"

"I begged her to come. . . . I'm still hopeful, but she made no firm promises. She's an unpredictable woman."

"She's an interesting woman."

"I don't know what it is, but there's something shadowy in her life. A secret no one is privy to."

"Gossip is against the rules," I said, cutting her off with a smile.

"Let's go to my room," said Sophie, who wanted to change her dress.

As she put on her dark blue velvet skirt, Sophie brought Mrs. Danielian up again.

"Her serenity made a deep impression on me," I said. "Something in her tranquil smile has a strangely calming effect."

"Do you really think she's all that calm? I wonder whether that isn't just a mask. It seems to me that there's a huge, an infinite sadness about her . . . but why? It's that 'why' there's no explaining."

Standing in front of the big mirror, Sophie arranged the thick plaits of her hair in a wreath around her head. She was silent for a moment, preoccupied by her preparations. Then she leaned toward me and said, "You know what?"

But just then the doorbell rang. We cocked our ears, trying to guess who it was, and hurried back to the drawing-room.

It was already late when Mrs. Danielian appeared. The guests had formed different groups in the drawing-room and were ardently discussing all sorts of questions. I myself was involved in a heated debate with some young writers; I was trying to dispel the sincere, sometimes fantastical skepticism that those young people too old for their years felt duty-bound to display. All of them, as if they were the sworn enemies of impossible dreams, wanted to glory in their impotence and try to erect the kind of ivory tower that I consider a prison for my restless, perpetually unsatisfied mind.

I broke off the debate. Involuntarily, my attention settled on Mrs. Danielian. She was wearing a plain black crepe dress and her hair was gathered in a bun at the nape of her neck. With a smiling, joyful face, she distributed greetings as she made her way through the room. A spreading, penetrating smell of roses lingered as a trace of her passage. With each step she took, a more pungently aromatic wave billowed up and rippled outward.

Hrant Cherkezian and an elderly gentleman entered the room on her heels, conversing as they went. You would have thought they were sauntering down the street, oblivious to everyone else; yet when Miss Varvarian came toward them, Cherkezian looked up like someone who'd just been awakened, and his eyes smiled for a long time, admiringly, at Sophie's beauty.

Mrs. Danielian approached to greet me, stopped, and said, "The organizing committee for your exhibition has been formed. The president is Vahan Diran Bey, a very good choice." The conversation immediately turned to me and my paintings.

My cheeks are on fire and there is a strange agitation in my heart. As we draw steadily closer to the day my work will come face-to-face with the public, an inexplicable emotion verging on fright is taking hold of me. I have never had this feeling in foreign countries, although the paintings I exhibit abroad are exposed to the gaze of people who are far more knowledgeable and much harder to please. There, simply being deemed worthy of interest is a triumph. Here, the very problem is different. Will I, I wonder, manage to break out of my spiritual solitude and renew some of my severed ties?

The room, the flowers, Sophie's lovely features, people's faces, Mrs. Danielian's smile—everything melts together and whirls around me, as if in a confused dream. An unfamiliar wave of stormy feelings wells up from my soul's depths and buffets my thoughts this way and that. Is it the hope of success? Or is it a presentiment of some other, unfamiliar thing? I do not know. I may become a leading personality in the renascent, resurgent Armenian community from one day to the next. . . . It seems that it is my task to utter one of the cries of liberation of a people that has for centuries been groaning under a crushing burden of violence and servitude, relying on the force of my personal talent and my inner, individual strength. That feeling uplifts me with such elemental force that all pleasures and sorrows, all the typical womanly ambitions and disappointments, seem like a handful of ashes beside the splendor of a flame soaring skyward.

At present, my artist's pride overrides everything else. I note with indifference the way people's admiring attention focuses on me. I, now, am the person at the center of attention. Sophie's beauty or Mrs. Danielian's charm is ignored; all the guests throng around me, as if hoping for a look or a smile. As if I were a new revelation, people's gazes are charged with feelings of all sorts. I sense that every gesture of mine finds a tremulous echo in their souls. Art embellishes me and sets a halo over my head. It seems that from now on, every step I take will be a step on the road to glory.

They are still discussing the organizing committee. The exhibition is to take place in the halls of the Alliance Française. They are discussing the committee's president as well. Vahan Diran Bey is a highly cultivated art-lover of refined taste, the grandson of a well-known government official; he comes from a Catholic family that has a tradition of patronizing each and every manifestation of Armenian art.

Abruptly, I don't know how, attention turns to other matters and new conversations break people down into little groups. Mrs. Danielian, after joining a discussion about a recently published volume of poetry, wanders off alone. I watch her closely. At present, her head tipped slightly to one side, she is looking around her with a smile, and it seems that her affectionate, loving eyes with their luminous gaze are gradually becoming moist. The fine delicacy of her temples is not yet marked by the least wrinkle, but the influence of the years is manifest in a look of general fatigue that leaves an impression of very delicate, very vulnerable fragility. With his measured tread, Cherkezian approaches the back of her armchair. They begin exchanging a few words in private.

Gradually, Mrs. Danielian's voice attracts people's attention and the private conversations cease. Talk gravitates toward the recently published volume of poetry again. Mrs. Danielian speaks for a long time, elaborating her views. I watch her very closely. She seems to have undergone a metamorphosis: this isn't the woman I saw on the landing nor the woman who walked into the room this evening in her black dress as if trembling with emotion. Now she is a self-assured, poised intellectual who fluently and effortlessly speaks her mind, setting out from solid foundations and drawing logical conclusions. Her clear, moving voice is a pleasure to hear, even for those of us who aren't following her argument. In the pink light of the lampshade, her forehead appears smoother and more luminous, and the gray threads in her hair now seem meaningful.

Once again I think to myself: What richness, what magnificence has here remained infertile! Everything that exists, all those seeds that will one day flower, could embellish the aesthetic life of a discriminating people. Yet all that is dispersed; each seed is isolated from the rest and deprived of the vital fluid that would allow those capabilities to swell and bloom in proportion to the strength contained in them from the beginning.

My tormented curiosity seems to have found the explanation for the sadness flowing over people's faces.

Perhaps in order to dispel the increasingly palpable anxiety, Sophie sits down at the piano. Her fingers run over the keyboard. Everyone falls silent and listens.

All at once I feel tired and drained. I rest my head on the headrest of my armchair and listen; my thoughts run off in a loose reverie. The scent of roses becomes sharper and I understand that Mrs. Danielian is passing by. Cherkezian is standing alone in the shadow of a curtain at the other end of the room, and it suddenly occurs to me that he hasn't uttered a word. . . . Why is he so stern with everyone? Does he feel no compunctions? Why is there no explaining Mrs. Danielian's behavior toward the person Sophie told me about? Why is everything so complicated and mysterious? What hidden recesses people's souls have in this singular city! Even I . . . why was I so gay when it seems that I'm now on the verge of tears? My nerves are jarred by the overwrought atmosphere of the room, the music, and the scent of the roses, with which, apparently, all of us will remain intoxicated forever.

In the shadow cast by the curtain, Cherkezian approaches me. The music has ceased. "Shall we go? I'll accompany you. It's late."

Mrs. Danielian lives near us, and the three of us leave together.

The sun has just risen and the bell of Holy Cross Church is pealing. There is a scent of incense in the air and my breath is heavy with the sun, the light, and the fragrance streaming in through the open window. I've gotten up very early, and with feverish emotion, as if driven by some danger, am now standing in front of my self-portrait and looking at it. It's me and it isn't. A woman from times long past seems to be smiling at me from within the frame. Yet it isn't just her profile that is familiar to me; her soul is, too. It's as if that human manifestation has been taking form and disappearing from time immemorial in order to find its culmination in my own form, which, however, will most assuredly not be the last.

Have I succeeded in capturing the color of my eyes? It is so inconstant: sometimes dark, almost black, and at other times so bright as to seem colorless. The greenish blue folds in my dress, whose color is reproduced in my eyes like a shadow, make the portrait resemble that of a Byzantine princess, the more so as it was painted after an illness: the emaciated face, the eyes with wide pupils and thin brows arching over them reinforce the impression. The lips, however, do not have the pallor of an ancient portrait: yearning and a sort of desire play over them, anxious and astonished, as on the face of a woman the morning after a day of deep emotion. It is the face of a woman who has plunged into the depths of an abyss, and having seen and heard everything, is now climbing toward a summit.

If only they could see everything that I wanted to put in that picture, rather than focusing on its intentional incompleteness! If only they could discern the suffering and the longing for a fatherland that has always held my soul in its throes, instead of seeing the young woman, the physical personage! Dare I hope that they will?

The church bells are still pealing. I seem to hear the morning hymn "Morning light, righteous sun . . . shine on me." A feeling of magnificent beauty washes over me in the pure dawn light. It's as if everything around me had undergone a metamorphosis.

I wander through the room from one painting of mine to the next. Here is a large landscape: a flat expanse of land, divided in two by a road that disappears in the distance; a solitary cypress towers over the scene, the treetop tipped slightly to one side. I am that cypress, too, standing on that interminable road, a road that disappears into the hazy distance without going anywhere in particular. I am—and my soul is— this spring picture, too, in which the almond trees are blooming beneath a sky heavy with clouds. I am the boat adrift on a sea whose waves with their pink foam seem to flower and fade without end, all the way to the indigo horizon over which a red cloud stretches like a wrinkle. I am this woman waiting expectantly at a window for her unattainable dream, her back turned on the opulent comfort of her room. My many-faceted soul strives for expression and representation. Yet over every one of my paintings there also hangs a helpless sorrow, because all that has yet to hear the all-encompassing word that I carry deep inside me; everything is mute and shrouded in fog, like a cloudy morning before the sun comes out.

A pathological shudder comes over me, a sign of fatigue and despondency, and I sit down in my armchair, facing the window through which all-powerful nature responds to my anxiety with its manifold, opulent, luminous beauty. The crises precipitated by my ambition, my upward flights full of faith, and then heartbreak . . . such is my life. Why am I not like other women? Why can't I enjoy the tranquil peace I see in so many others who are born, live, and die without ever knowing themselves? Where did I acquire my taste for the impossible, which holds me in a state of perpetual emotional turmoil and impatience, so that I sometimes ask myself why I am so sad, or why I am so happy? It is as if, in my soul's secret depths, there occur successes and defeats whose last waves alone reach me.

The reason was perhaps my childhood, spent in a warm, loving environment. I was brought up like a princess, they say, protected from all the bitterness of real life. When I first felt the world's harsh breath, I was like a greenhouse flower suddenly exposed to the rude climate of the outside world. Those hothouse days of affection and boundless love fostered the pathologically delicate sensibility that makes me perpetually uneasy and anxious and has bred my fervent wish to aspire to something beyond day-to-day goals. This predisposition has been the source of my greatest joys and misfortunes. Exempt from immediate cares of all kinds, surrounded by a providential, painstaking solicitude, I lost a feel for real life; and my mind and imagination acquired the habit of soaring freely toward the abstract realm of dreams. That is how it happens that, sensitive and unarmed, I abruptly found myself face-to-face with life's harsh necessities while yet preserving in my soul's depths a longing for, not the comfortable life I had led in the past, but the dreams I had cultivated then. For me, they were more real than life itself.

The upshot of all this was the enthusiasm and indefatigable earnestness with which I embraced art. Art was the place where I sought to embody my dreams, the place where my moods became color and line, and where my inner harmony, incomprehensible even for me, struggled to find expression.

In art, I sought to discover the paths to people's souls, to learn to communicate with others, to confer the rhythm of my dreams and emotions on their shapeless, colorless feelings, to orchestrate scattered songs ringing out in isolation, to conquer the artist's invisible, omnipotent realm, to become one of the peaks towering over the human plain, and to contemplate, not just the totality of present possibilities, but that which is to come as well, that which belongs to future generations and is as yet, for the vast multitude, a vague, amorphous, impossible dream.

What is this ardent ambition based on, and how can I justify it? Am I like those vainglorious, pretentious people who are blind to their weaknesses and treat their inadequacies with indulgence? By no means! No one can discern her own weaknesses as clearly and mercilessly as I; they drive me to despair. But I have forced myself to wage an unending battle. Why? Who compels me to? My infinite desire? Perhaps. Yet there have been moments when I sincerely wished to free myself of this compulsion, descend from the cold solitude of my ideal, mix with ordinary people, feel their joys and little victories, and live and die like so many others, narrowing the horizon of my desires.

Yet it seems that there is, inside me, some fateful thing independent of my will—a call to play the arduous part I believe I must play. This is an incurable predisposition whose origins escape me and whose conditions I obey, almost unconsciously. And I am proud and feel that my ego is solitary and strong. I observe it sometimes with admiration, at other times with apprehension, at still others with anxiety.

It is difficult to explain the mixed feeling of pride and humility that stems from my calling and the inadequacy of my means. Sometimes I seem like a stranger to myself, with strengths deep inside me that are the more frightening because they remain hidden. At other times I feel that there are bottomless abysses in my soul, that I stand on the brink of them awaiting revelations, and that all the doors to simple joys and simple sorrows are swinging shut before me.

Despite all that, however, in moments of weakness and despair, a voice murmurs to me: "Why? Perhaps all that is only illusion, hallucination . . . a vain conceit or simply overwrought imagination. Why withdraw into the solitude of your vocation? Why chase after unattainable glory? You are young and beautiful. Life has blooming gardens for those who keep their feet planted firmly on the ground without trying to fly toward impossible horizons."

In those hours of temptation, I see a loving couple walking hand-in-hand down a sunny path in a garden full of blooming roses, murmuring tender words to each other.

It is a May day awash in light. The hot weather has already arrived. Buzzing without pause, multicolored ladybugs are dancing round and round in the sunbeams that, like columns of light, penetrate the curtains into the room.

Today they are making rose jam at home. With the gravity of a bishop getting ready to celebrate Mass, my aunt, dressed in white from top to toe, is engaged in that complex, delicate task. On the divan, which is completely covered in white, roses are piling up, sorted according to quality: some will become jam, others will be used to make syrup, while leftover bits and pieces of petals as well as the very tiniest petals will go to make rose brandy.

Wearing her glasses, my aunt, with her nimble white fingers, snips off the white tips of the petals with a pair of scissors. A fragrant pink wave is rising on the tray. Not just the room, but the whole house and even the street is full of the pungent, penetrating scent of roses. It is an excess of fragrance; the maid, another woman who has come to help out, and even my aunt, their heads spinning from a mild case of rose-poisoning, have to interrupt operations from time to time and leave the room for a breath of fresh air. But the smell of roses pervades the whole house, the stairs, and the kitchen, where some of the petals are already boiling away in wide-mouthed copper pots.

Sitting cross-legged on the divan opposite my aunt and thinking back to past days, childhood days, I watch that delicate, beautiful operation. Making rose jam is a task that calls for taste, experience, and patience, and has its successes and failures. The scent of the raw roses must be preserved. Only a lady of the house with long experience knows the secret of the right moment, when a certain quantity of rose petals has to be blended in with the thickened sugar syrup, a step she carries out intuitively and with concentrated attention. My aunt is silent and engrossed; she doesn't like to be interrupted or distracted, and breaks her silence only in order to issue short, curt orders.

Preserving the roses' color is another major concern. On this question, opinions differ. My aunt has no desire to try new things. She respects tradition, doing everything the way her mother and grandmothers did. Using a deep, potbellied kettle, she steeps the petals that have been gradually cleaned and collected in lemon juice. Working by instinct and measuring by eye, she performs the entire operation with dexterous gestures, absorbed by her sacred task. Because syrup-making requires less care, she puts that off. I cannot observe the fine points of her work without a certain admiration.

"Leave the room; this is no place for you," says my aunt, who is worried on my account.

In the spacious room in which I've hung my paintings, the roses' unrelenting fragrance pursues me, saturates me. The air I breathe seems to grow thicker and makes me tipsy. Dizziness, a sudden malaise, rubber knees—and the reflection of my face in the mirror is pale, blanched white, even if my eyes are burning with fever.

I get dressed in a trice, leave the house, and cross the broad street in Bağlarbaşi, leaning on my umbrella the whole way, because my malaise refuses to go away despite the sunlight and fresh air: I carry the intoxication of the roses' pungent fragrance in my nostrils. The whole neighborhood is permeated by that smell. It is rose season and many different houses exhale the gradually diminishing aroma. Slipping out of open windows and doors standing ajar, the fragrant wave spreads through the air, while the ladybugs, entranced by their favorite flower, buzz in the sun and fly every which way, instinctively trying to find their way to the roses piled up on divans, trays, and tabletops.

Today Vahan Diran Bey, the president of the organizing committee, will be calling on me.

A quick visit with Miss Varvarian. We leave the house together and stroll across the flowery fields as far as the promontory. On the way, we encounter Mrs. Danielian, sitting on the ground in the sun with a book in her hand, her back propped against a tree trunk. In its shade, we are inundated by milky light that is aflutter with big spots of sunshine. We, too, plop ourselves down on the ground. We are unable to speak, having abandoned ourselves to the delightful dominion of the light and warm air. The others suggest that we go as far as the Bulgurlu Fountain, but I'm in a hurry to get home and prepare to receive my guest.

We eat a hasty meal, because my aunt has not yet finished her work.

"Did it come out well?" I ask.

My aunt hesitates to say something definitive, although her face displays the satisfaction of someone who has got the better of a difficulty. "It's still hot, it's too early to say," she answers. "But I think it did."

The maid brings rose jam for us to taste in small crystal dishes. It is wonderful. This is not eating, but rather feeling, assimilating what is the most intangible and fleeting for our senses: aroma and color.

"That's not jam, that's poetry," I say to my aunt, who suddenly beams with pleasure, her kindly, wrinkled face turned in my direction. Her eyes are still beautiful, full of light and wisdom.

Then we talk about Vahan Diran Bey. She is acquainted with his family. Indeed, in the old days, when my aunt was a young lady, their families spent time together. She tells me that family's tragic story.

Diran Bey's grandfather was a rich, influential gentleman, one of the leading members of the Armenian Catholic community, when he became a victim of Patriarch Avedik's persecution. The Armenian Patriarchate, aware that it was powerless to stop the spread of Catholicism, fell back on violent, insidious methods. Patriarch Avedik won the Sultan to his cause by persuading him that the Armenian Catholics were agents of European powers and traitors to the Ottoman state. After pronouncements of anathema and moral sanctions, the bloodthirsty Patriarch, his hand strengthened by the government's raw power, published a decree requiring every Armenian Catholic to attend Mass in an Armenian Apostolic Church the following Sunday. His aim was to distinguish the rebels from the repentant.[3]

The small Armenian Catholic community, whose freedom of conscience was thus violated, comprised the most civilized, enlightened social stratum in Constantinople at that time. As a result of protracted, unjust persecution, it had attained a certain spiritual and moral elevation. The Catholics met in the homes of their community's leading members for Low Mass.

The consequence of this passive resistance was collective exile, accompanied by loss of legal rights, incarceration, and so on. Leading families went bankrupt and many government officials were driven from office. There was not an Armenian Catholic family that did not have its exile and its prisoner. Diran Bey's grandfather and his two brothers were dealt the severest punishment because they stood in direct relation with the French Embassy. Wealthy men who had led a luxurious, refined existence, showered with honors by the Sultan, they preferred to give up everything, and after refusing to appear before the implacable Patriarch, were condemned to death. Their immovable assets were confiscated by the Palace and their families and children lost all they had from one day to the next, preserving, with their sanctified martyrdom, nothing but their good name.

The coach stopped in front of the door. I made out my guest's profile through the curtain.

We got acquainted in the drawing-room. He gave me a long, thoughtful look that lasted a little too long. I, for my part, was smiling. At that moment I thought to myself, "How bare this room is. It seems to be furnished with nothing but wall-hangings. All that must change."

Diran Bey and I remained standing face-to-face. My surroundings appeared so vast and bare to me that I seemed to be losing my freedom of conduct and movement. I sat down on the low divan, which my aunt had covered with an old-fashioned Lahore shawl in honor of our noble guest. I listened to him with my hands clasped on top of my right knee. I am aware that, against the colorful backdrop of the Lahore shawl, I form a harmonious whole in my dark blue outfit, with its open collar and sleeves. My hair is arranged so that it rises toward the top of my head in waves. It must, I know, be gleaming in the strong afternoon light.

After flooding the room until noon, the sun has now disappeared behind the roof. There is a singular shadow in the room, because it seems that the walls, wall-hangings, and everything else are still emitting the radiant light of the sunbeams they had soaked up earlier. That may be the reason that, unexpectedly, a flash of light pulses brightly and then dims, or a color presents itself more intensely to our eyes. Suddenly, the rose that is blooming in its vase sheds red, intensely red petals that fall to the floor; or one of the designs on the wall-hanging covering the wall seems to detach itself from the background, dancing before our eyes with its embroidered zigzag and then fading away. . . . A strange torpor has come over me and it is as if I were in a dream . . . . The conversation is halting, we are having trouble making it flow. We are, no doubt, observing each other. I would like to paint his portrait; yes, I think to myself, that is the reason for my distraction. I would like to penetrate that face's secrets and its unequaled charm. It seems to me that, with my eyes closed, I could see it more clearly in my mind's eye.

The banal conversation characteristic of first encounters comes to a close when my aunt walks into the room. She has donned the black dress that she wears on special days; it is set off with an artfully embroidered white collar and cuffs. She has a truly elegant demeanor and gait, with her white, still abundant, slightly curly hair and the wrinkled, honeycomb-colored skin that makes her black eyes stand out. She has a particular way of receiving guests that she reserves for those capable of appreciating her grace and elegance, typical of the customs of a bygone day.

A short while later, the tray with the jam appears — silver, with a barely perceptible blue intaglio design. With its color and aroma, the rose jam in the little dishes of transparent Saxony glass carries the day.

There is a regal, ceremonious aspect to all of this. While Diran Bey and my aunt are busy refreshing their memories of their progenitors' relations, I, now relaxed, observe my guest.

Diran Bey is the sort of man who could make his way through a crowd without attracting attention, because only people of discernment can appreciate his unusual traits and, especially, the singularity of his face. Slender and somewhat taller than average, elegant but not affected, with finely chiseled features, blond hair that has begun to go gray, and a pale complexion that perhaps owes its pallor to the bloodlessness typical of scions of old Constantinople families, he bears the marks of an aristocratic lassitude on his face. His small, honey-colored eyes, closely framed by the arch of his blond eyebrows, are hidden behind gold-rimmed glasses. His forehead is broad and seems taut, but it is unwrinkled; it is so transparent at his temples that the network of his veins shows through. The somewhat too long oval of his face culminates in a little beard that is now shot through with gray. His aquiline nose, with its delicate nostrils, puts the crowning touch on that face, while under his little mustache, very fresh and clear-cut, the flawlessly formed lips are smiling and supple, fostering a surprising feeling of intimacy and tenderness.

It goes without saying that no woman of discernment could remain indifferent to that blend of delicacy and strength, that elegant simplicity and harmonious facility of expression. Yet something else commands my attention: I experience an unaccustomed feeling of peace and inner harmony. It is as if all the unsettling voices in me had fallen silent; as if, now, the flighty impatience that makes my mind skip from one thing to another without letting me linger for a moment over a single impression had ceased to exist. It is as if I wanted constantly to say: "yes, that's it". . . "yes, that's exactly right". . . his words, his voice, his gestures, the smile on his lips, his pensive, dreamy gaze—everything appears to correspond to my inner, secret harmony, which, it seems, has only just now been revealed. . . .

Am I happy? I cannot say, but a sort of pleasant torpor has captivated me. My brain is no longer functioning, or it has been switched off by some inexplicable inner feeling and is losing its power of control. An instinctive, irrepressible pleasure bewitches me; it is uninhibited, albeit still dispersed. It is a kind of unfamiliar force which, I feel, is hovering over me and has not yet mastered me, although I have neither the power—nor the desire—to escape it.

Diran Bey abruptly turns toward me. "Since the light hasn't changed yet, Madame, would you like us to look at your paintings?"

An unexpected fear takes possession of me, together with a sort of shyness. I would prefer to keep my work—an expression of the many different facets of my soul destined to be exhibited before the multitude—veiled from that one man's eyes, revealing it to him only by degrees. That feeling is paired with another: although I am fairly thick-skinned where other people's opinions are concerned and have already attained a certain indifference, I suddenly become as trembly and irresolute as a child, lowering my eyes to the floor to hide my confusion. . . .

Despite my fears, we go into the other, larger room. Fate comes to my rescue: Miss Varvarian arrives in the nick of time. She, too, would like to accompany Diran Bey on his visit. She is happy, smiling, and as lighthearted as a butterfly. Her good mood infects us all, and although my words are still disordered, I manage to maintain a certain composure. When Sophie takes my arm and tugs me from one picture to the next, punctuating her questions and observations with funny stories, gossip, and irony, I laugh nervously with her. My soul, however, is full of apprehension, agitation, and churning emotion.

"What's the matter with you today, Emma, are you sick?" Sophie asks all at once.

Diran Bey turns toward us and a wave of blood surges to my face. At just that moment, a sudden gust of northern wind makes the curtains flutter, and the evening light trembles. We deeply inhale the fragrance of the wisteria that has climbed up the sides of the house . . . a feverish emotion goes shivering through the air . . . we exchange strange, penetrating looks, as if wanting to speak, while Sophie steps closer to a painting. Only with effort, however, do the words reach our lips; they are not formulated easily as they come surging up, and there is something strained in the way we are acting with each other.

We are standing in front of my self-portrait and I wonder, anguished, whether he likes it or not. Why is he looking at me so intently and with such emotion? We walk over to the divan against the facing wall and sit down side-by-side.

"Madam, the motive for what I am about say to you is not just courtesy or a wish to be obliging. I approached you and came to see your work with uncertain feelings."

An iron fist seems to have my heart in its grip and my feverish cheeks are on fire.

"I heard about you a long time ago. These past few days, people have often talked to me about you and your work, but . . ."

A different kind of sun seems to illuminate the room, and we are in an altered atmosphere. I listen to his voice with anxious impatience.

With emotion, but without haste or embarrassment, he goes on: "And what I have seen here in your house, what I have felt . . . exceeds all my expectations."

Diran Bey," I suddenly declare, surprised at the unwonted quiver in my voice, "I am particularly touched by your approbation."

I turn to him and we exchange another long, deep look. There is something indefinable in that gaze: it seems that it has brought us into a deeper, more spiritual communion.

Thereafter, he talks more calmly and methodically about his impressions. Since my return to Constantinople, this is the first time that I've talked with anyone who has a truly cultivated taste for painting. His judgment is clear and goes to the heart of things.

"You seem to be familiar with painting."

"I myself have never painted, but I like painting very much. With much love and great care, I've put together a collection of Byzantine icons. If you honor us with a visit, I would be delighted to show you my little museum."

"With great pleasure, Diran Bey."

Sophie's laughter startles us. We turn in her direction. She's leaning out the window and laughing at I-don't-know-what. It's late and the light in the room is fading. The rustling of the trees in a nearby garden floats up toward us; the air on my lips is heavily scented, and from all sides the scattered elements of an omnipotent beauty seem to be making their way toward my soul in order to embellish this moment of my life.

"There is intelligence and restrained power in your art."

"Oh, Diran Bey . . ."

"It doesn't seem as if a woman's hand had held your brush; your portrait, for example . . . only a man could have painted it that way. I find it difficult to formulate my feelings and thoughts at present, but this much is clear: only a man is capable of painting a woman affected by her most tumultuous, most electrifying emotions."

"Diran Bey . . . I'd like to talk about art with you again some other time, at greater length. I'd like to subject my work to more severe scrutiny with you after you've freed yourself from the influence of your first impression. No one has ever spoken to me the way you have. . . . I myself can't clearly express my thoughts at present."

I suddenly lifted my head and looked at him. He answered my gaze with a seemingly more intense emotion and I saw a shiver pass over his lips: words formed without being uttered.

Sophie approached us, interrupting our conversation. She stood there for a moment, and smiling mischievously, looked at me and Diran Bey by turns. Then, suddenly planting herself opposite us and looking at my portrait, she said, "It's so good; it's good, isn't it, Diran Bey? I think it's Emma's most successful picture."

"It's good," Diran Bey repeated after her. "It's amazing; it's as if I'd already seen that picture somewhere. It seems that those eyes, that face . . . that profile is not new to me."

With Sophie, I ushered my guest to the door. On the other side of the garden fence, in the shade of the rose bushes, Diran Bey turned back toward us one more time and waved at us both before taking a seat in his coach. I went down the steps with Sophie and we went into the garden.

"Emma, Emma," Sophie said, jokingly. "Diran Bey . . ."

She said no more, but I understood, and saw the meaning of my emotion. She never learned that she inaugurated, at that instant, with those words, one of the stormiest, most beautiful, and most painful chapters of my life.

Everything passes away, everything disappears. Our feelings for one another, too, could not *not* come to an end. Whose fault was it? Most assuredly, not mine and not his. . . . How long our love was to last was determined by the impulse it received in that first moment, and it ceased just like that, with no good reason, amid a sweet murmur, like a spring rain on trees in lovely blossom.

Months and years have gone by. Tonight I am remembering the emotion on his sweet face and the radiance of his beautiful affection. Then, I felt that my soul had been liberated, because it was only then that I felt myself in close communion with the infinite and the unknown. There were moments when happiness and joy delivered my mind from the bonds of reason and space. There were moments that filled me with the cold, sublime feeling of hours without end; and there were moments of suffering and sorrow that rolled by as slowly as the centuries. Now, however, all those moments have melted together, and only the intensity of the emotion they once contained gives them meaning.

Today, when I take my palette in hand, my joys and sorrows come back to me and my brush is guided by stormy inner emotions. Every day and every hour, I relive those bygone moments; they present themselves to me with a smile or a tear, and I immortalize them. The people who pause in front of an artist's works cannot imagine that we have to relive a past grief a hundred times, that we have to make our hearts bleed a hundred times, in order to be able to communicate to the apathetic, indifferent multitude passing by the impression that grief left on us when it was present and real.

Standing before my easel in front of the blank canvas, I vainly seek to capture in my imagination the vision of that fleeting time. Memories invade my soul, shattering its immobility. . . . It's as if the thoughts I once thought have vanished, along with my mental anguish. My exiled soul believed it would discover unbounded horizons, because, for a moment, joy and sorrow opened all the doors that had been closed before its restless, anxious impatience. Today, however, my brush once again hesitates on the canvas . . . and I feel that I am returning to my inner prison, which now is decorated with nothing but memories and desires.

It is better to lay everything aside and go pay Mrs. Danielian a visit. I may find Hrand Cherkezian there as well. . . . His severe, reproachful gaze may soften when he sees in my eyes the longing for new springs, the longing for life, whose wave of light mixed with shadows is surging up around me. . . . He may feel, as well, that despite my self-assured solitude, despite the confidence with which I had set out on what I thought was a flight toward freedom that would distance me from them, we are again, as always, companions in exile, inmates in the inner prisons we have built ourselves, each of us the other's merciless jailer.

The afternoon sun, cooler now, is sinking on the horizon. A shepherd's flute sounds from the distant valleys. Wisps of pink clouds are slipping swiftly through the sky. It is better to remain alone and listen to the murmurs of my heart; that I make my way to the remotest recesses of the garden beneath the blossoming cherry trees, whose white petals, in moments of such great beauty, came raining down on us.

Translation by G. M. Goshgarian

First published in Vienna by the Mekhitarist Press in 1922. Translation based on the text in Volume 2 of Zabel Yessayan's *Works* (*Yerger,* in Armenian), 2 vols., issued by the publishing house of the Armenian Catholicosate of Cilicia, Antelias, Lebanon, 1987, edited by Shushig Dasnabedian.

NOTES

1. A reference to the period immediately following the 1908 Young Turk Revolution and the restitution of the1878 Turkish Constitution.

2. A 1909 anti-Young Turk "counter-revolution" attempted to restore the power of the Turkish Sultan. It was marked by anti-Armenian pogroms in Adana and other regions of Cilicia. The "counter revolution" failed, and led to negotiations for an electoral alliance between the Turkish Committee for Union and Progress (Young Turks) and the Armenian Revolutionary Federation.

3. The Armenian Patriarch of Constantinople Avedik (1704-1706) is known for his persecution of Armenian Catholics; subsequent Ottoman policies toward Armenian Catholics fluctuated. Following a period of persecution in the 1820s, an Armenian Catholic millet was formed in 1831, giving the community religious autonomy.

My Soul in Exile, or Art in Bondage

This essay first appeared as a "Postface" in Zabel Essayan, *Mon âme en exil* (Marseille: Editions Parenthéses, 2012), pp. 65-75. It is reprinted here with the permission of the publisher.

By Krikor Beledian

Translated by Catherine Carpenter

A rather strange work. A novel as compact as a short story, and of a disconcerting simplicity. An elegant story, steeped in perfumes and flavors, and flooded with the light of an idyllic Constantinople. A pointillist painting or watercolor. A text, a voice—that of a woman painter, calm and true to herself. No crises, no incidents. Yet nonetheless, under that apparent calm, what profound malaise! Here amid the splendors of an ancestral residence where everything breathes internalization and rootedness, whose walls are covered with paintings, she speaks of exile and isolation. The chained soul does not inhabit her body, nor her place, nor her art. Absent from herself, she is there without being there.

Zabel Yessayan is at the very peak of her art when she begins to write *My Soul in Exile*. Something of the genesis of the work is known, thanks to a letter Yessayan wrote from Baku on September 23, 1917:

> At this moment I am plunged into all kinds of work. As soon as I get a little freer of it, I'm going to start on a novel about the life of Armenians in Constantinople, entitled *Hokis aksoryal (My Soul in Exile).* I am full of my novel's subject, and whenever I am alone—which rarely happens—I isolate myself in that corner of my soul which shelters my novel's universe: in that refuge there is neither massacre, nor deportations, nor Bolsheviks, nor anything else, but only sunshine, roses, and the eternal song of love, beauty, and grace. If I could manage to give expression, even if only partially, to that secret world, I would be satisfied, very satisfied.

Almost everything is said in those lines. Nostalgia, the hindrances to her art, the Armenians' catastrophic situation, the nightmare of annihilation. In this connection one needs to know that Zabel has been back in the Caucasus since September 1915. Thanks to her determination, her skillfulness, and to the favorable circumstances called good luck, she has escaped the arrest of writers and intellectuals—her companions—most of whom disappeared into the camps of Chankiri and Ayash in Turkey. She survived that disaster. After a lengthy journey which took her from Sofia to Varna, Petrograd, and Tiflis (Tbilisi), she bursts into action. As someone who has miraculously survived, she wants to bear witness to what she calls a catastrophe, a crime, or the annihilation of an entire people, and which she herself has already witnessed in 1909, in Adana. In the Caucasus, she gives lectures concerning deported writers, stirs up public opinion, meets with journalists and supplies them with documents. From 1916 on she collects the testimonials of the survivors of the deportations. Harrowing work, she says, but necessary. She transcribes Haig Toroyan's account, which she publishes in the review *Gordz* of Baku in 1917, under the title, "The Agony of a People."[1] She interviews another important personage, Murad of Sebastia. From the long odyssey of that former guerilla (fedai), she drew her *Murad's*

Journey (1920). Another large collection of testimonials, which are mentioned in her correspondence, never sees the light of day and disappears without any other trace.

It is within the framework of this omnipresent testimonial literature, in its particularly stressful context, one rather unpropitious for creation, that the writing of *My Soul in Exile* takes place. The text, in two separate parts, appears in the review *Areg* of Berlin-Vienna in 1922 and then, the same year, is published as a single volume of 32 pages. Is this the predicted novel? The letter quoted above and the choice of title leave no room for doubt. The passages to which the letter makes allusions can easily be found.

Even so, can one call it a "novel"?

Indications of genre are rare in Yessayan's work. One exists for *Meliha Nuri Hanem* (Paris 1928, 38 pages), which has the sub-title *"veb"* (novel) on its cover and title-page. Is it a provocation? Is there in it a willingness to move beyond the limits of the novel? What separates a novel from a long short story or a fleshed-out tale? Obviously the use of the term "novel" by the author of *The Gardens of Silihdar,* at least in this context, has nothing to do with obeying strictures about length. It seems to relate more closely to the novelistic itself, to what makes a text a work of fiction. In passing, I would like to point out that nothing can be understood of Zabel Yessayan's protean production if one does not take into account the immense effort she expended in experimenting with new forms of writing.

Thus, in "Reflections on the Novelistic Genre," revised during her years of exile in Paris and published in Smyrna (Izmir) in 1904 in *Arevelian Mamul,* Yessayan distances herself from realistic and symbolist novels. She goes so far as to define her own conception: "The novel should no longer be the description of a fait accompli (that is the role of History), it should no longer be only the reflection of life, but life itself."[2] All of the young Zabel Yessayan's thought revolved around her clearly stated refusal of a simple representation *(badger-atsum,* in the text) of real facts, such as adventures or possible and impossible crimes. She takes pleasure in mocking what she considers to be photography, in opposition to which she sets painting. A very *fin-de-siecle* opposition, but significant nonetheless. The painting theme dominates *My Soul in Exile.* Before taking that up, let us say that the proper goal of novel-writing is neither to reproduce the real nor to create imaginary events in order to strengthen the plot. It is a question not only of offering a "reflection" of life but equally to create life. The novel is life. That is the equation. And thus novelistic is not in the least reduced solely to the "novel" form, but to the capacity of writing to give form to life from the narrative point of view. It is fiction in so far as it reflects an essentially individual vision of the world, and thus perforce subjective. This is why what is called a "narrative plot" shifts from objective reality toward the depths or onto the sensitive and sensual skin of the first-person narrator.

Therefore I will refer to *My Soul in Exile* as a story, or even perhaps a poetic recital written in the first person in which feelings and impressions make up the essential framework of the narrative. That genre has found definite favor among the Symbolists whom Yessayan reads and has some contact with in Paris. The numerous prose poems and short stories which she publishes, more or less irregularly, in Constantinople newspapers between 1895 and 1908 and even beyond, are distinguished by a freer and more inventive style than the realistic writing which was widely favored by her Armenian contemporaries. The exploration of a subjective vision of things and a pronounced taste for synesthesia (sounds, scents, colors) display a certain impregnation with the symbolist aesthetic. Although sedimentary, in the text that aesthetic clearly rises to the surface. A minimalist plot, indeed a lack of any plot, a reduced cast of characters, a few significant scenes interspersed with moments of ecstasy, reflections, affects, and a manifest willingness to describe not the world but one's own perceptions of it—all those are characteristics of that specific kind of writing.

Yessayan imposes the poetic recital form on her work from the admirable *Twilights of Scutari* (1906), which pushes the travel-notes genre to its limits, and afterwards to *Hours of Agony* (1912-1924) and *The Last Cup* (1917), i.e., in a series of works in which the writing eschews the classic narrative scheme and is wary of the fetters of the novel. But in practice the writer is far from being so univocal as suggested here. In fact, she never manages to divest herself completely of the seductive attraction the traditional novel has for her. *When They No Longer Love* (1914), *The Obstacle* (1920), *Retreating Forces* (1924), *Shirt of Fire* (1935), or *Uncle Khachig* (posthumous, 1966) are more and more concerted and less and less convincing attempts to present a complex reality within a form already largely proven.

The year 1922, when she is living in Paris and publishes *My Soul in Exile,* is a pivotal date. Turning her back on her prior political commitments, she takes a position in favor of Soviet Armenia, to which she gave concrete expression by her assiduous collaboration with the pro-Communist journal *Yerevan.* In 1927 she traveled to the Soviet Union, from whence she brought notes for *Prometheus Unbound* (1928), a work of propaganda designed to seduce the "proletariat" of the diaspora and which adheres completely to the line adopted by the party in power in Soviet Armenia.

The Communist regime's ideological preoccupations render a subjective approach to reality nearly impossible, and the writer seems to adapt herself to this scheme of things. Torments of the "I," the "unhealthy" states of being, introspection—all are "narcotics" for the working class, she maintains in a letter to the writer Zareh Vorpuni (May 1927) on the occasion of the publication of *The Ordeal* as a short story (1925). Therefore the "I" would be sacrificed on the altar of proletarian literature. When Yessayan settles in Yerevan in 1933, she is thinking exclusively of the realistic novel. That's what she talks about to Hagop Oshagan in a 1935 letter.[3] She has in mind *Uncle Khachig,* which she is then working on. In that work she returns to the social concerns of pre-war Constantinople (the class struggle is not far away). There is, however, one major exception: *The Gardens of Silihdar* (1935), where she once again uses the first-person poetic recital, but in the guise of "romanticized memories." Autobiography seems to win out, but in fact is instead being liquidated. The writer is in the process of taking stock.

Therefore *My Soul in Exile* occupies a central place in Yessayan's work. It marks an end to her subjective work, almost a writing-down of the Self, until that kind of writing is disowned. Before stigmatizing it as contradictory, it would be more just to understand what it is at play here.

Described as a whole, the poetic recitals take up again a certain number of themes common to works from before 1915: the artist who has emigrated or been exiled to Europe and returns to his/her native country (the Ottoman Empire, Constantinople) but cannot manage to become part of that reality which excludes them or where they feel exiled. This thematic structure is already in place in *Twilights of Scutari,* which tells about a first such return, that of an anonymous female narrator (Zabel?). An analogous configuration is found also in *The Novel* (1914), where the primary character is a novelist who leaves Paris to live once again in the Ottoman capital, which he ends up abandoning after the failure of his "psychological" novel.

The Emma of *My Soul in Exile* is therefore of the same family. She is an artist, as was Zabel's husband, Dikran Yessayan, who died in Paris in 1921. Fully as much as photography and painting are opposed to each other, so do literature and painting have a perpetual mutual attraction. Painting transformed into a metaphor for writing and serving as a pretext for reflections on art is not hard to find in Yessayan's work. But pictorial art can yield place to the art of the savory when perfumes and colors melt together into an unctuous, entrancing substance. The scene about preparing rose jam in *My Soul in Exile* will be read with delectation; it is an unusual scene in many respects, and is, beyond the local color, an allusion to art understood as the subtle alchemy of sensations. It is certainly the case here that the artist, moving from exaltation to disappointment, discovers that internal exile is omnipresent in all those around her. Exile a commonplace? Not to be where one ought to be, to live always at a distance from oneself, from one's body, from one's art, from that Constantinople society by which one is made welcome, but which is not really a society at all. Exile a sort of non-being?

Emma arrives in Constantinople sometime after the Adana massacres. Yessayan in Baku hears of the catastrophe unfolding in the distance. The parallel is obvious. One is always on the periphery of abnormal events. The narrator and the author find themselves confronted with the same problem: what place does art have in a period when the very existence of the community itself is threatened? What happens to the artist when social, economic, political, and "national" concerns take precedence over an art defined as essentially an individual experience? After 1909, after 1915, is there even a place for art? Here is found one of Yessayan's recurrent themes: the conflict between the individual and society, between what one wishes for and what the law allows, between the search for self and the fate of others. Zabel is known to have little enthusiasm for feminism, the problem for her being less that of woman per se and more that of the single individual hindered, bound, and oppressed both by and in society.

Emma's story reflects the disarray of a writer deeply involved with testimonial writings but dreaming of a Garden of Eden. Later on, in

1935, already settled in Yerevan for two years and in the middle of writing *The Gardens of Silihdar,* Yessayan confirms her obsession: "In my lifetime I have seen many countries and all kinds of marvelous things, but for me the memory of the Gardens of Silihdar remains indelible. Those gardens have been with me everywhere, and I have taken refuge in them every time black clouds have darkened my horizon."[4] Odd avowal for a writer who seems to have fitted quite smoothly into a new life and to have wanted to cut her ties to the past. But Emma, who hoped that her soul would be freed from its chains and find itself again in fulfilling work, discovers that her horizons are closing in on her again. The sole and unique time when she glimpses an end to her exile is the love of Vahan Bey. Love the antidote to exile? A bond other than the communal? And yet, on the subject of love, Emma's monologue maintains a deafening silence. That silence is itself the obstacle to the continued course of the text. Emma says nothing. All is finished, the exile continues. She looks over her paintings, which certainly have the appearance of unfinished works. Did those shared feelings fail? Were they a delusion? We will never know. Exile is present where a being is absent from herself.

A sense of community is lacking. It was already threatened in 1909 when Yessayan wrote her irreplaceable *In the Ruins.* The threat becomes reality in 1917. Testimonial writing takes precedence and functions as a "duty," as a commitment for which the author renounces her beloved literature. She considers any attempt to make literature out of the suffering from millions of deaths as a "sacrilege." There will not be another *In the Ruins.* Admittedly, *Meliha Nuri Hanem* treats of an episode in 1915 and does this following a purely subjective aesthetic, but the "novel" comes to a sudden end, a bit after the fashion of all Yessayan has tried to write about her flight from Constantinople.[5] Literature, a mourning for herself.

After the Adana catastrophe all of Yessayan's writing gravitates around the risk of annihilation faced by a people dispersed, divided, and massacred. As with Daniel Varujan, as indeed with the whole group connected with the review *Mehian (Temple)* in 1914, it is an obsession. Literature will be possible only when the question of being-together has found an adequate response. In any case, without a people reunited, brought back together, and bonded, there is no art.[6] This renders understandable the profound meaning of Yessayan's reversal of opinions in 1922 and her adherence to Communism (in fact it was more like joining a guild). It owes nothing to opportunism nor to some sort of ideological capriciousness, both of which she was accused of by her political adversaries.

The ordeal of a faltering community or of a displaced people seems certainly to have been a determining factor in a kind of panic passion for a new form of being-in-common. Faith in a different society, a better humanity, a new man freed from his chains, of which the travel notes in *Prometheus Unbound* celebrate the advent, form an important part of the search for a politically reinvented community. To escape from imprisonment within oneself by means of the invention of a being-in-common under the name of proletariat or working class seems to have been the essential requirement. A utopia's function is to make the topos, the place, possible. More clearly than is generally thought, Yessayan understands this perfectly, and her character Emma keeps repeating that the price to pay is simply to renounce one's individuality and one's art. An unrestrained community, i.e. one absolutely itself, without anything missing from it or any breaches in its walls, is that not the end of the individual and of art as the creation of that individual? The road to subjection is not long, it is only torturous. Imprisonment reinvents itself. Stalin's prisons are populated by the deported and exiled. The infernal cycle begins again. As for Emma's gardens, their roses, their many fragrances, their light, the delicacy with which they are designed and experienced, evoke an elsewhere both obsessive and futile. It is well known that the counterpart to exile is nostalgia. And from nostalgia is born fiction.

NOTES

1. Recently published in French translation by Marc Nichanian, *L'agonie d'un people* (Paris: Classiques Garnier, c2012).

2. *The Twilights of Scutari.* Istanbul, 2009. p.257.

3. In his monumental work, *Panorama of Western Armenian Literature* (in Armenian), Hagop Oshagan (1883-1948) devotes an important literary study to Zabel Yessayan. (Beirut: Hamaskaine, 1968), vol. 6, pp. 245-348.

4. *Les jardins de Silihdar,* French translation by Pierre Ter Sarkisian (Paris: Albin Michel, 1994), p.30.

5. The unfinished "A Writer's Memories," which appeared in the journal *Hayasdan* of Sofia in August 1915, attempts to reconstruct the few weeks that Zabel lived clandestinely with the poet and critic Ardashes Harutiunian. As a precaution, the characters are not named; the text is signed "Viken." Moreover, the journal itself, along with Zabel's text, was to cease to appear when Bulgaria entered the war on the side of the Central Powers, with whom the Ottoman Empire was allied.

6. I cannot here continue to reflect on the possibility/impossibility of an art of the diaspora. The savage opposition which Yessayan manifests in 1931 towards the Menk group and the idea of a literary community says a great deal about her essentially territorial, perhaps even statist, conception of such a community. See my *Cinquainte ans de literature arménienne en France: du Même à l'Autre* (Paris: CNRS Editions, 2001), particularly the chapter entitled "An attempt at creating a literary community: the *Menk* review," pp.105-29.

Early Works

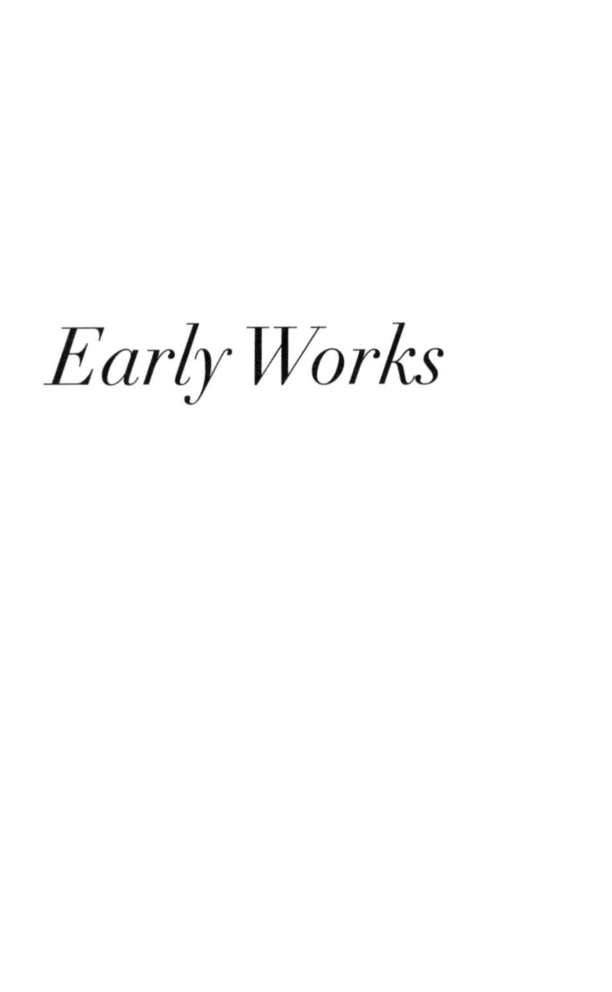

Ode to the Night

Come, O night, come, cover the world with your black skirts, subdue the last breath of twilight with your coolness, cover the world in your funereal darkness.

The day enters your somber breast in its tomb, dragging along with it all the feelings and concerns sprouting within.

Loving hearts anxiously wait for you to smother their reveries in your darkness. Come, close their weary eyes with your invisible fingers. Take them to the depths of slumber for a few hours.

Resting on your black arms, take them far from the daily routine that has exhausted them. In your coolness, lull them to sleep with your sweet music. Let their worries melt away for a few hours in your solemn realm.

Your arrival brings with it precious memories. You are a friend to the lonely. It is you who sees the most private tears.

The sleepless, miserable individuals who pass by open windows take in your cool darkness.

Their thoughts and feelings wander around in your breast. And you take them all, burying them in your consoling obscurity.

Translation by Jennifer Manoukian

This poem, written at the age of seventeen, is Zabel Yessayan's first published work. It appeared in the first issue of Arshag Chobanian's literary journal *Dzaghig*, No. 1, 1895, p. 17.

Feminine Souls (Honest Love)

On cold nights when the wind, galloping outside the window and whipping the life out of the dry tree branches, makes the window panes shudder; and when the rain falling from the night sky clings to the darkened window panes like drops of molten silver, Verkine, her eyes fixed on the dense darkness beyond, listens to the music of a winter's night.

Her teeth chattered from both the room's temperature and her emotions. Their mechanical sound became one with the music of the night, having fused with the sighs, cries, and sobs of nature.

She felt with all of her being that she, too, had a role to play in the night's song.

Since the impenetrable darkness around her gave her the chance to rest, she worked on analyzing every feeling that passed through her soul.

The most powerful force within her was love, and she saw music as its most worthy recipient.

And now, swaying to nature's music, she joyfully counted all the directions her life could have taken since adolescence had she not persevered.

Verkine was very young, but nevertheless endowed with conviction, enthusiasm, and a fiery imagination. Beyond the erratic emotions of her heart, she felt that her soul yearned for more immaterial worlds. Real-life emotions, even those considered to be the most noble, still could not satisfy her soul. She felt as if she was tarnishing her heart by attempting to feel emotions that were incapable of renewing her enthusiasm for life.

She had encountered all the prejudices of her family and neighbors, but did not feel the need to tolerate them. For all the worthless morals that they had thrown at her, she had only a derisive smile. Her soul remained impervious to all of their chatter.

Graced with a free mind and a free heart, this young girl rebelled against our society's absurd social order and, never fearing the ignorant tyranny of public opinion, lived according to the needs of her soul and of her heart, convinced that in the future society would not give her all that youth had lavished on her.

But at the same time, despite the passion and youthful vigor that drove her in life's fierce race, she never succumbed to smiling or flattering charmers, for she felt that a few days of pleasure were not worth all the disappointment and misery that would inevitably follow.

She wanted to find something that would renew her enthusiasm for life each and every time, something capable of moving her, exalting her soul with noble, sublime emotion.

And because she felt such an enthusiasm, such a fire in her veins, she had to take advantage of it by all means; otherwise it would take advantage of her. She therefore wound herself around music, like ivy.

True happiness, that slow sweet joy that music brings, Verkine felt completely. Her soul was able to grasp its wistful emotion and lofty impulses; slowly, drop by drop, the music drove her to intoxication, taking her soul prisoner with more force than any other intoxication.

From afar, a few undulations of a vague, approaching melody were enough to move her. All the blood rushed through her body; with her head throbbing, her expression trancelike, her lips trembling from her soul's passion, her cool hand passed across her burning forehead, as if to feel the dreams soaring within.

Her love for music pushed her to study the divine art, to produce with her fingers her soul's greatest emotions.

Among the instruments, she chose the violin: an instrument which spoke to her heart in a quiet yet commanding voice, sobbing softly or singing with the purest emotion, and in whose most delicate undulations lay muffled, weeping sighs.

Since she directed all of her desire, all of her dreams towards this goal, she was able to realize it. She had such ambition, such blazing passion! How many times did she listen to the shrieks of the violin strings under her untrained fingers, content with the mere illusion of being a gifted player?

Despite spending long hours alone with her violin, she never experienced boredom that might disturb her enthusiasm. She knew that her false notes were necessary for making melodious music in the future. In her recurring dreams, the violin took the form of a small boy sobbing.

The initial challenges passed quickly and she made visible progress. Now the bow's light touch on the strings produced sweet and regular melodies.

A year passed. She could now express all her soul's sweet, lovely emotions, through the vibrations of the strings.

With the violin pressed tenderly to her heart, as if the object was in need of a caress, she tuned the strings one by one and listened carefully, dreamily, to those imprecise, irregular sounds produced by her fingers' contact, all while imagining the melodious sounds that would soon be heard. With the same tenderness, she gently placed her violin under the velvet, enjoying its rough coldness on her skin.

The fingers of her right hand were already positioned to flutter across the strings. Holding the bow lightly in the fingers of her other hand, she placed it on the strings, waiting with sublime anticipation for the burst of sound upon the bow's first contact with the strings.

And the melody began. Beyond art, there was emotion in its undulations. The music rose and softened, while the bow continuously whirled lightly over the strings; the fingers of her other hand pressed the strings instinctively, as if electrified by excitement.

Intoxicated by the melody, her soul was gradually transported to a world of reverie. Everything melted around her, as if becoming invisible. The walls collapsed silently in a barren place where every connection to the world was slowly suppressed and faded away. Only light and shadows lengthened, leaving their gold and black silhouettes behind them.

All the undulations of the music took life and traveled towards her like rippled waves, the pleasant waves of the final notes enveloping her entirely.

The melody seemed to flow independently from the violin and added to Verkine's sweet illusions. She strolled in a dream world, surrounded by calm music from a distant and immaterial place and by songs sung by lanky ghosts, their gauzy skirts swelling in the pure white space.

At that time, all the sad aspects of her life passed before her eyes, one by one, like wandering ghosts. There were some blurred, smiling faces mixed with flowers, fragrances, and colors, but the ghosts all eventually faded into their infinite chain, veiled in a light fog.

As always, through the vibrating air, a woman swathed in veils emerged. On her milky white breast, she held a bouquet of roses; smiling, her hair blowing the wind, she slowly rose in the air. Victoriously, she placed her feet on top of this hazy world in which all of Verkine's life was buried. Fragrances emanating from her hair, from the roses covering her breast, and from her entire body were visibly spinning the exceptionally transparent air and the rippled waves traveling towards her became music so sweet, so intoxicating, that even the woman, stimulated by her own fragrance, extended her arms towards Verkine.

Translation by Jennifer Manoukian

Short story published in *Dzaghig*, No. 5, 1895, pp. 192-96.

The Red Windmill

A poem in prose

Gloomy premonitions dazed me with their somber dance and my soul, suspended in morbid inspiration, was thrust into the center of an illusionary world.

There, everything was black. Souls in mourning slid through space like a swarm of bats. Around me I heard dirges; the smell of burning hearts intensified in the darkness.

There, heartbeats reverberated and produced a frightening melody that resembled an owl's cry. I too became a piece of this darkness, imprisoned in the infinite obscurity that engulfed the entire space.

And so we wandered, almost without sensing the darkness. In its depth, giant buildings lifted their aerial foundations and let us pass through without any difficulty. An atmospheric whisper directed our journey, which became a dance, a crazed, monotonous dance made up of linked shadows. Tugging at one another, we circled around something with desperate, senseless, unconscious excitement.

A cold light left a ray in the space and before our eyes appeared the red windmill in motion.

It was a giant windmill, the very top of which disappeared into the shadows. It turned constantly, and with each turn the creaking of its invisible wheel, ending in a prolonged moan, was heard in the echo. Red blood gushed from all sides, as if from each one of the structure's pores, and gave the impression that the windmill was formed from clotted blood.

In the distance, sinister mouths opened and responded to the sobs rising from the depths of the windmill with peculiar bursts of laughter.

What were they cutting up in there? What were they crushing?

Our dance was much more frantic now and, little by little, the frozen ray illuminated the structure with more intensity.

It was then that I saw them throwing hearts inside.

They threw and threw. They threw those blackened and pierced pieces of flesh, many of which were charred and reduced to practically nothing, at a baffling rate. The more they threw, the greater the number of black, mourning souls became. The whisper echoed and completely overpowered the uttered cries, laughter, and songs.

How did I allow them to absorb my entire being? How did their injection dissolve me atom by atom? I continued to watch the hearts that they were throwing inside the windmill, hearts sometimes still fresh and red.

Suddenly I felt a sharp pang, like the fading of my irresolute existence, and, among the hearts inside, I noticed that they were throwing mine

I looked around me, dismayed and emotionally stirred, when I saw His eyes directing the windmill from above with His gaze.

Translation by Jennifer Manoukian

Published in the periodical *Anahid* , No. 1, 1898, pp. 40-41.

The Man

Memories from My Student Years

For Adrushan[1]

"In terror, there is a kind of sublime, delightful pleasure," a friend once told me, showing me Adrushan's beautiful article in *Masis.*[2] It is as if all of our senses suddenly awaken. There is something I don't understand in that limitless, intoxicating feeling of panic, something that often only lasts for a moment, but whose memory continues to vibrate in our souls.

We argued a bit. Yes, the most overwhelming, powerful, intoxicating feeling was terror; I could accept that. But I could not accept the idea that terror could bring about pleasure. And in order to explain what I was saying, I told my friend about something that had happened to me, about a memory from my student years that often comes to mind.

It was the beginning of my second year in Paris. At that time, I lived on Boulevard Arago in a small room on the sixth floor overlooking a courtyard. The courtyard and the buildings surrounding it created a small square-shaped shaft as deep as a well. From six stories high, I couldn't see the ground. That shaft was dotted with small windows from which the nauseating smell of poorly prepared food would waft out twice a day and constantly hang in the air. Above me, all I could see was a square-shaped sky, and that too was often covered by black, noxious smoke from the nearby factories or by a cheerless, muggy haze. When, once in a while, I would see the blue of the sky, my soul would fill with childish joy; in those moments, it seemed that all people needed to feel pure, unadulterated happiness was a bright, blue sky.

Sometimes from the depths of the courtyard, through the stench of cooked meat and suspicious greasy particles that coated the four sides of the shaft, the voice of a singing vagabond would rise and take hold of the area. Whenever I heard him, I would put my work aside, go to the window, and dream. Oh, how I would dream. If the strangled, sobbing sound of a barrel organ would reach me, I don't know why, but a strange sadness would pass through my soul, and I would feel a sentimental urge to cry in my dark, gloomy room.

I felt hopeless and bitter, and I was entirely alone to bear it all and ruminate on my worries. In that sad, freezing room, I would look out the window at night and feel as though I was on the edge of a dark, gaping pit. In the house, workers and their families lived on the first five floors; the sixth floor, made up of small rooms, was entirely occupied by foreign students—sad, blonde girls who would wearily trudge up six flights of stairs. Yet on their pale, melancholy faces, the light of vigor and determination shone steadily and continually in their eyes.

We would smile at one another and even say hello sometimes, but I didn't have any kind of relationship with any one of them. At night, when they would all gather in one room, I would listen to the wistful, heartbroken cadences of their foreign songs, or to the weak, tender vibrations of the mandolin. And only during those hours did all of my strength, all of my unshakable ambition, all of my fanatical determination to persevere melt like a snowflake, and I would feel the chill of despair in my soul. Oh, that soft staccato of the mandolin. It is as if its debilitating vibrations will always stay with me, and remind me of my weaknesses and disappointments in my dreary room on Boulevard Arago.

I've said that at the time I was in a hopeless, bitter state, so it's easy to understand when I say that not one of my compatriots ever came to visit me. I would spend days, sometimes weeks, without uttering a single word in my language. (It was in that state that I lost my habit of thinking in Armenian.) I had a few foreign acquaintances, but almost all of them were also students, and extremely busy with their exams. As a result, I lived a more isolated existence than ever before, and outside the time I spent working, I immersed myself in the writing of Edgar Allen Poe. For quite a while, I read a lot of Poe, and Baudelaire.[3] Their books were the ones on my night table, and before going to sleep, I would slowly recite a sonnet from *Les Fleurs du mal.* It was as if these sonnets were an intoxicating, unsettling drink I would consume drop by drop. I'm saying all of this to more clearly express the emotional state I found myself in on the morning Miss Zavatska—one of my foreign friends—came to my room, pale and terrified.

"Oh, you have no idea. You can't possibly understand the strange thing that just happened to me. I can't stay in this house. I just can't anymore. One of these nights, my terror and fear will kill me."

Almost sobbing, she muttered some incoherent words, among which I could make out only "Terrifying! It's something really horrifying."

Miss Zavatska was a lovely young girl. She was a literature student like me whom I met in Deschanel's class. Very blond and very dainty, Zavatska suffered from a malady of the chest. Her years were numbered and she knew it. What I didn't understand—really couldn't understand —was why she had decided to spend her fleeting youth in one of Paris's poor, student neighborhoods. In other words, why was she enduring a life full of hardship and deprivation, when the depth of that life, containing a bitter, special kind of pleasure, would be entirely inaccessible to her shy, wistful, delicate soul?

So Zavatska told me what happened:

"The other day after midnight, there was a knock at my door. I woke up suddenly and shouted, 'Who is it?' There was no answer. Naturally, I said to myself that I must have heard the noise in a dream and confused it with reality. Who could it really have been at that hour? I stayed awake for a short time and listened to make sure no one was there. I didn't hear anything, so I fell back asleep. Some time had passed when I awoke suddenly. There was someone at the door again! This time I listened, my heart pounding. The bell of the Broca Hospital across the street rang three times. It was three o'clock in the morning! My forehead was drenched in cold sweat. A feeling of alarm and danger seized me once more, but again I thought, 'There's nobody there. It just seems like it.' And I was just about to convince myself of that, when this time I heard three powerful thuds on my door. In that moment, everything around me was so silent that the city almost seemed empty. My heart was beating so hard that, for a minute, I thought the thuds I had heard earlier had been my own heartbeats. But no, there was no way to confuse the two. The three thuds on my door were much louder. And at the same time, I could hear a man breathing—a rasping, muffled, ominous kind of breathing. What could I do? My room was pitch black, but opening my eyes wide, I could slowly make out the outline of the furniture. And during all that time, I sensed that there was someone outside my door. I stayed like that—tense and terrified—for a while. The breathing soon faded away, and I heard muted footsteps, as if someone was walking carefully in socks. I couldn't sleep for the rest of the night, and when morning came…"

"Wait a minute," I said, interrupting her. "This is a kind of fear a child would describe, Zavatska. Surely it was a flirtatious neighbor who had seen you, and thinking you were one of the girls from the factory, wanted to try …"

"I thought the exact same thing once it was light outside, and I heard that everyone in the house was awake. Thinking about the night before, I saw that there was nothing in the room to make it seem as if anything had happened. It's even funny to tell people about something so vague. But fear had already been sown in my heart, and the following night it was hard for me to get to sleep.

"I woke up as the Broca Hospital bell was ringing midnight, and I'm sure it was for no reason at all. But all my senses were in such a state of excitement that it was as if I was hearing a cacophony of noises and seeing bright, ever-changing shapes. Suddenly the same soft, dull sound of footsteps—I don't know where they came from—approached my room. Yes, it was the exact same sound. There was no doubt about it. Soon I heard the same breathing—muffled and ominous. It was as if I was hanging off a cliff; I felt the same strange feeling that would often overwhelm me in my dreams. Instinctively, as a way to protect myself, I had lost the ability to sense the passing of time, but a couple of thuds jolted me back to reality.

" 'Who is it,' I shouted without thinking.

" 'Miss,' a voice outside the door stammered. 'Can you lend me some matches? Please, I beg you. I'm completely in the dark.'

" 'I don't have any,' I said abruptly in a dry tone.

" 'Miss, I'm your neighbor. If you do have some, could you please lend me one or two, because I forgot to get them and...'

"And then I heard the sound of my lock, which he was turning in vain. I had drawn the bolt, but I was sure that ruffian, that criminal (who knows what he was) could somehow get the door open. Lying in bed, I was as cold as a corpse, and my limbs had cramped and stiffened. I wanted to get up, get dressed, open my window, and call for help, but I couldn't do anything. All these ideas passed through my mind, ran through my mind, without having a single effect on me.

"And I stayed like that for I don't know how long. There were a few more attempts to open the door until finally the raspy breathing faded away, and the footsteps disappeared into the nearby courtyard.

"In the morning, I went downstairs to complain to the doorman.

" 'All of your neighbors are upstanding people. Something like that couldn't have happened,' he told me. Yet I explained what had happened in greater detail. It was the absolute truth. But the man shook his head stubbornly.

" 'It couldn't have happened, Miss. No one could have done that to you.'

" 'But…'

"His wife came in, so I had to tell the story again. This time, they started to laugh as if what I was saying was funny.

" 'What a strange girl! It's all in your head. Who in this house would want to come ask you for matches at three o'clock in the morning?'

"And one by one, they listed my neighbors—decent people in their mind. I didn't know any one of them.

" 'Fine,' I said to myself once I left the house and found myself out in the fresh air. 'I seem to be ill.' I was subjected to surprising nervous weaknesses, but my God, everything was so clear. I wanted to see my doctor and be treated for it, but I couldn't find him. Last night, I reluctantly returned to my room, but luckily Miss S came and stayed with me until midnight. I didn't tell her anything, but after she left, I drew the bolt and made sure it was secure. Then I drank a lot of rum to try to fall into a deep sleep. I fell asleep as soon as I lay down.

"Again? There was no question this time that there was a man outside my door, because I could see a very distinct strip of light in the narrow gap between the door and the doorframe. I knew it. Almost panting, the man worked to open the door. There was no way not to believe it. I heard the soft, careful sound of his tools, especially the gentle, rhythmic scraping of his file. And then," Zavatska turned entirely white, "the door opened. It was still dark, but humid air from outside rushed into the room like a torrent, and the breathing drew closer—the raspy panting of a wild animal, carefully and softly tip-toing his way towards my bed.

"In the morning, I found myself sprawled out on the floor. I had fainted and had been there for hours. My entire body hurt and my limbs were as stiff as a corpse's. Once I remembered what had happened, I jumped up terrified. I don't even know how I got myself dressed, but it was certainly hastily because my clothes and sheets were thrown everywhere.

"My door was closed as usual and the bolt was in place. I don't know how it could be. I came straight here. You have to understand. I can't spend the night there. It would be impossible. Impossible!"

Zavatska, terribly distraught, started to cry like a little child.

I thought for a moment. I could easily believe what the poor girl was saying. She had a look of genuine terror on her face, but there was something about her story that also inspired some doubt in my mind.

"Was everything in the right place when you woke up in the morning? Was anything out of order? Your drawers or anything like that?"

"Not a thing. Everything was in exactly the same place, except for me. I had fallen onto the floor with my sheets."

"And you said that the door was bolted from the inside."

"It definitely was. I checked before I opened the door to come see you, and I was surprised."

"You know, Zavatska," I said holding her cold hands, "it seems as if your mind might have been playing tricks on you these past few nights."

"Oh, no, no! Don't talk to me like the doorman did. You have to understand what I'm saying."

"Fine, do you want me to come over tonight and stay with you?"

After some hesitation, Zavatska accepted my offer.

Naturally, it wasn't my courage I was relying on to get through the night. I was convinced that Zavatska was having a nervous breakdown. Fear had never penetrated my soul until that point; I had never been subjected to a truly gripping, deadly kind of terror.

And yet all day I thought about what had happened to Zavatska. If it was true, the idea was like a poisonous bite that shook me to my core many times over.

In the evening, we had dinner together, and after going for a walk, we came back to her room. By the time the water for tea had started to boil on the alcohol burner, we seemed to have forgotten everything, and started telling each other about memories from back home—sweet, fragrant memories. Mine were bright and shone golden in the sun, and hers were calm and tender like a melody. We were so far from home and so foreign to each other, yet we felt so close in that moment, almost like sisters. There was so much shared affection in our words, and in our gestures.

Poor Zavatska, do you remember the night the doctor's prediction came true? When nothing, nothing more, remained of your dainty, blonde head, or your clear, bright eyes?

When it came time to go to bed, we had completely forgotten about the nightmare that Zavatska called *The Man* in a special tone of voice, and we even started making jokes about it.

"Now let's go to bed and wait for *The Man*."

"I'm sure *The Man* saw you and now won't come tonight. You'll see!"

"Thanks for the compliment, Zavatska. Am I so terrifying that I can send *The Man* running?"

"Oh dear, I didn't mean it like that."

Later, to get me to go to sleep, Zavatska made me drink a half a bottle of rum almost by force. She drank the rest.

"I'm so drunk," I told her. "It wouldn't surprise me if *Men* started appearing before my eyes. I'm sure you're feeling the same way."

This time I was right. The room was filled with cigar smoke, and after I drank the half-bottle of rum in one gulp, I felt like everything was spinning in a bright circle dance around me.

I was lying down on a big armchair across from Zavatska's bed. We kept talking after turning out the lights, and because I was trying to convince Zavatska to ease up on the strong drinks, she tried to convince me of the opposite, saying:

"Rum, you see, is harmless and so useful for poor students. In fact, if rum hadn't existed, I wouldn't have been able to last this long. It's true that…"

A deep, heavy sleep pulled my eyelids shut.

I awoke suddenly, and sat up in my bed.

"What is it?" I would have said had my tongue not felt so thick in my mouth. And instead I fell silently back onto my pillow. Zavatska was sleeping soundly. Why did I wake up? What was wrong, I thought to myself? The room was pitch black. Having opened my eyes like a blind person, I had scanned the entire room in vain before noticing a long, bright strip of light near the door. First it was flickering, but it became steady, and I could hear the scraping of the file—soft, but determined—on the iron lock.

Suddenly the idea that what Zavatska had told me was true filled me with such a strange, vague sense of unease that I felt as if I was being set aflame one minute, and the next I felt a cold sweat creeping up my spine and making me shudder.

Back in reality, the city was silent. It almost seemed deserted. Only the sound of wagons rumbling sinisterly in the distance could be heard from time to time. And at our door *The Man*—this time real and ominous—was grinding his file on the iron lock. Zavatska—feeling safer with me in the room—was still sleeping, and I didn't dare try to wake her up, or to have her share in the terror that was gradually growing in me and making me insane.

Slowly the door started to creak. Yes, that couldn't be denied. And *The Man's* low, raspy breathing was now synchronized with the sound of the grinding metal.

Then the file stopped. I stared at the door, my eyes wide open. The strip of light flickered, and then vanished. At that moment, I can't even express the utter terror I felt. It was a kind of terror that seemed to freeze the blood in my veins. And at that moment, the door opened. In the darkness of the room, an even darker silhouette appeared and slowly came towards me. A gust of freezing, humid air rushed in through the half-open door and froze the sweat on my forehead. As still as a corpse, I stared at the black silhouette, which was silently inching closer. I wouldn't have thought this shapeless blob was human, if not for the wheezing, shallow sound of his breath, whose warmth I could practically feel on my frozen face.

It was as if those were my final moments alive; I felt that the terror I was experiencing in that instant was about to kill me. If it had not been for the beating of my heart, which was pounding so hard in my terrified body, I would have thought that everything had ended for me.

The Man came even closer, and as the minutes passed, I opened my eyes wider in fear until I realized that, in my attempt to see everything, my eyes were shimmering in the light, and that *The Man* could see them. I shut my eyes, and beneath my tepid eyelids, I sensed that my pupils also were frozen. I don't remember how many seconds, or hours, all of it lasted, but when I opened my eyes again, a sad, pale sunrise had given everything a hazy, gray hue. And *The Man* wasn't in the room. Zavatska was still sleeping. A little while later, I heard reassuring footsteps on the stairs. I wanted to get up, but I couldn't. And I put my exhausted head back on my pillow.

When Zavatska woke up, she wanted to joke around again.

"Didn't I say that tonight *The Man*…"

But turning to me, she suddenly got up, and anxiously asked:

"What is it? What's wrong with you? Why are you so pale? Tell me what happened!"

I caught a glimpse of myself in a shard of a mirror, and I was as white as a ghost. My teeth were chattering, and under my eyes were big, black circles.

"Zavatska, you shouldn't stay in this house. What you said is true."

After that, Zavatska had to stay in the hospital for a few months for her nervous breakdowns and frequent delusions. *The Man* had appeared repeatedly during these breakdowns. I also suffered for a long time, and the truth is that even now I don't know if *The Man* was real or if I had simply found myself inside of one of Zavatska's nightmares.

Translation by Jennifer Manoukian

Published in *Masis*, No. 5, March 26, 1905, pp. 68-73.

NOTES

1. Adrushan is the pen name of Simeon Yeremian (1871-1936), a writer and critic of nineteenth and twentieth-century Armenian literature best known for his 10-volume study *National Figures:Armenian Writers* (in Armenian).

2. *Masis* was an Armenian newspaper and literary journal based in Constantinople.

3. Charles Baudelaire (1821-1867), a French poet best known for his *Les Fleurs du mal* (Flowers of Evil), was also the first to translate the work of Edgar Allan Poe into French. It was through Baudelaire's French translations that Yessayan became acquainted with Poe's work.

Essays on Contemporary Issues

During the early years of the twentieth century, Yessayan published countless articles in the Armenian periodical press. Many of these articles dealt with the changing roles of women in contemporary Armenian society. Teaching was one of the few careers open to women at the time, and therefore many of her articles called upon the community to support those educators; she insisted that teaching was a respectful career path for women and not merely a pastime for wealthy and otherwise idle women.

With the 1908 revolution in Turkey that reestablished the Constitution and promised democratic and liberal reforms, Yessayan encouraged women to play a constructive role in the new society. Specifically, she called upon the more wealthy and privileged Armenians in the capital of Constantinople to aid and assist their impoverished and downtrodden compatriots in the rural provinces of the homeland, and believed that women and their organizations had a special role to play in this respect. The massacre and destruction of the Armenians living in the Adana region that accompanied the 1909 attempted counter-revolution in Turkey brought Yessayan to the area on a relief mission and strengthened her advocacy of efforts to improve the lot of Armenians living in the provinces.

Our Women Teachers

Among our working women today, teachers compose the majority. Each year we are seeing their numbers grow with the increasing demand both in the provinces and in Constantinople. This is an encouraging sign from many standpoints. First, it shows the gradual strengthening of our women's will to work, of their desire to be of service, and of their great hope in leading an entire community towards intellectual development.

Today's teachers have also put an end to the ridiculous stereotype of the old, ignorant, pedantic, and simple-minded woman teacher. Even if they still exist here and there, these old women, with their stern glances, contorted expressions, and suit of armor reinforced by many years of experience to prevent them from revealing any emotion or affection—that ugly, painful stereotype has been sentenced to death. This is good news not only for students, but also for the young women teachers themselves, who enter the field of education with tender hearts and a new sense of determination.

At one time, our harsh, intolerant customs would have ostracized these working women. They would have been practically stigmatized for looking to fulfill their desire to work outside the gentle, conservative environment of the family. Slowly, however, this has become a necessity. Working women today have become doubly noble to us, but prejudices still remain in the minds of many. I often have had the opportunity to reflect on the unjust, senseless disdain of which our women teachers, in particular, have become the targets.

Perhaps this prejudice has lasted until now because of the questionable intellectual capacity of many of the women teachers. But we must get to know them more closely in order to understand their level of responsibility in fueling this prejudice; often among these sickly, pasty-faced girls with hair whitened by eraser dust and bodies and minds exhausted, there are jewels of self-devotion and sacrifice who are suffering in vain from the pain of waning youth and the need for a better life.

I have seen women teachers who have worked at a school for years—arriving in the early morning and not leaving until the evening—driven by the nagging concern of earning a living, and many times burdened by parents incapable of earning one for themselves. They stay silent in the face of all the unjust attacks showered on them by school trustees and parents. Seeing the image of their financially insecure futures pass in front of their eyes, they readily submit to the schemes of their more powerful colleagues. Young women at the start of their adult lives quickly take on the appearance of crushed, old women, pale from malnutrition, with worn-out voices and tired eyes; these women, grieving the strict need to conform, are supremely unhappy and give the impression of being dried-up, barren tree branches.

There are some who have already been demoralized by disappointment. Strong and self-confident, they enter the field to do something important, to use their knowledge to fulfill a role in the field of education. Having a professional path in mind and clear aspirations, they begin teaching, but here they encounter mean-spirited calculations, dirty gossip, and a sense of contempt, all of which serve to discredit them. At certain times, motivated by the sense of moral decency inherent in their role, they resist all of this, but eventually they almost always give in. Some have remained in the field, their hopes shattered and hearts broken, as little by little they grow accustomed to the accepted norms and gradually suppress their better instincts.

This is why, when there are constant complaints here and there about our women teachers' insufficient knowledge and sometimes even about their moral quality, we must immediately stop to think about who is directly responsible for this situation, before showering them so liberally with insults and reproaches.

Today, the work these teachers can do is severely limited. They form only one important wheel of a machine. In the task of instruction, everything is already arranged and plans are already prepared. They have a path to follow. Their entire job consists of following it and reaching a goal as quickly and as well as possible. For weak or mediocre teachers, this situation may be best, especially when we take into account the inconsistent and unpredictable state of our schools. But the ones who would have been able to do something on their own are trapped in a web of lesson plans and rules, making it impossible for them to express their individuality.

Sometimes an irremediable, contagious kind of viciousness or other situations arise among students, and teachers can rely only on their instincts to control them. The world's best theories and plans often become ineffective when they are implemented point by point. It is precisely the accuracy of these instincts that characterize a good teacher. Absurd stubbornness and surging anger poison the students' character, often by injecting the seeds of hatred and incivility into them.

The importance of teachers who can think and reason has been carelessly and inexplicably lazily overlooked in this day and age. Far from being just women for hire, they must be, and already are, the main contributors to the moral and intellectual health of our future generations. They hold in their hands the power to mold young minds. It is in interacting with friends that the ugly and beautiful facets of the students' characters emerge. In this way, only the teacher can remedy the ugly facets with the adaptability of her instincts, and bring out the beauty of the child's soul with a maternal kind of tenderness. Teachers and parents must mutually grasp the great importance of their work; instead of seeing one another as rivals, they should act in solidarity, without resorting to insults or contempt, in order to help and complement one other in the difficult task of educating children.

Translation by Jennifer Manoukian

From the newspaper *Masis*, No. 32, August 9, 1903, pp. 497-98.

The Newest Manifestations of the Women's Cause

The issue of women's liberation has resurfaced with new impetus upon the election of a woman parliamentarian, the Norwegian Mrs. (Anna) Rogstad.[1]

It would of course be unnecessary to outline once again the essence of the feminist movement when that is clear to all our readers. However, it would be worthwhile to examine what transformation the movement has been undergoing in recent times and to identify the causes for its new direction.

It is clear—and even the opponents of the movement concede—that we can consider the women's liberation cause won for the reason that feminism has almost entirely shaken off its features that are reproachable and irreconcilable with human nature; and further, instead of becoming the vehicle of expression for certain daring and exceptionally gifted women, it has become the greatest contributor to the social revolution. Without the liberation of women it is no longer possible to conceptualize any improvement in social conditions or an ideal for a future society.

Only in countries paralyzed by past glories and bound by prejudices is it believed that by oppressing and enslaving half the population it is possible to create a degree of bearable life. All the weaknesses and imperfections ascribed to women, on the basis of which shortsighted and petty oppressors justify their condition, are the result of the inferior position women have occupied until now. Throughout the years and centuries, the unbreakable chains that were placed around women's necks kept them at the mental level of immature children. Women have become crafty, cunning, lying, and groveling. Women saw the manifestation of their inner strength only in the role of a seductress; they thus became flirtatious, cunning, and it is not surprising that when the opportunity presented itself, women were unyielding in exacting revenge, and that with subtle wickedness.

Centuries of male tyranny—generously rationed over time—gave way to the exaggerations and unnecessary demands brought forth in the early days of the feminist movement that left it open to easy criticism; but over time, in civilized countries, women—owing to their high level of education—entered into their appropriate and correct path, and without much difficulty they soon gained their place in society.

Today, there is not one wise woman who will base the issue on principles of equality. Women and men have equal value, yes, but they are not equal or alike. This was a simple issue that in the beginning resulted in misconceptions. The difference in physical composition scientifically also brings about moral and spiritual differences. To insist that women can perform just as well in all male professions and roles was the result of feminist fanaticism; similarly it was wrong to insist that women—by virtue of their physical gentleness—were in need of constant care. To these arguments, one can accept the conclusion drawn by the renowned and enterprising French writer Mrs. Juliette Adam as the most accurate:

> Woman is not equal to man. She is as valuable as he, and she completes him. A society can only thrive when it understands what a woman and a man are.

Learned men, philosophers, and sociologists from different civilized cultures support this conclusion, which provides the overall thrust of the women's cause today.

Nature has already assigned the roles. No matter what dark and even primitive communities we explore, we see that the role of women in families is the same. Women have assumed the most selfless and perhaps even the most difficult role: educating their sons; and even in the most oppressed countries, a woman assumes her role in society when she becomes a mother. The reflection of the mother is evident in her child. Her will, her aspirations, her desires and ideals are pursued and actualized through her child, whom she arms with her moral values. In the theater of life, she remains behind the scenes, but what sort of oppression could prohibit her from inspiring her sons who were raised on her bosom? Is it not often that we see acts of heroism or examples of wise and virtuous lives that had a mother's tear or a mother's smile of satisfaction as their primary motivator?

A woman is and has always been omnipotent as a mother. No matter what life offers, whether circumstance and time corrupt or ennoble, the initial education—a mother's stamp—leaves behind inerasable traces on one's character.

Today's woman—with her high aspirations and multifaceted education—does not strive for anything but to widen her circle of influence; to come out of the boundaries of family life; to assume her role as educator and caregiver—freely and without limitations—side by side with her male counterpart, by complementing and completing his work.

A woman—whether a doctor, nurse, teacher, or lawyer—remains in her logical role; in the fast paced and unstoppable process of social transformation, she has to play her own unique and beautiful role; and she no longer needs to enter fields that are unsuited to her character and proper for men just to reaffirm her liberation. Alternately, as caregiver and mediator, activist and public speaker, the new woman is obliged to express the demands and rights of her sex, and to skillfully wage the sacred struggle of the oppressed. Women's efforts and activism are considered indispensable and valued contributions by all those driven by selfless and noble ideals, while those who criticize them have had no other motivation than the pathetic and cheap tactics of rivalry.

The election of Mrs. Rogstad is cause for rejoicing for feminists worldwide, because it opens the gates of a new arena for women's involvement; it provides a very beneficial forum for defending her cause; and it exalts the great significance of women's role in society.

Translation by Nanore Barsoumian

Arakadz, No. 1, May 25, 1911, pp. 3-4.

NOTE

1. An educator, women's rights activist, and politician, Anna Rogstad as a deputy representative of Jens Bratlie became in 1911 the first woman in Norwegian history to sit in Parliament. When Bratlie became Prime Minister in 1912, Rogstad held his seat full-time for a year.

The Armenian Woman after the Constitution[1]

In general terms, the declaration of the Ottoman Constitution brought forth the beginning of a new era in Turkish-Armenian life. It was natural that the forms, fields, and means of women's activities would also change accordingly. Without falling into the trap of extreme optimism, we will establish a new reality only when we can say that the new status quo allowed our oppressed, nearly strangled, spirited nation to breathe. But on the other hand and at the same time, it revealed the horrific, shocking reality that was created under the despotism of an unparalleled criminal.

No matter how many bits and pieces of information from outside the country or publications imported with much sacrifice revealed a nightmarish state of events based on imaginations over-stimulated by horror and anguish, the women of the capital could not truly fathom the reality of Armenian life in the provinces. After the declaration of the Constitution, once the shackles were broken, the doors to the prisons were opened, and our miserable brothers, reduced to exiles in their own homeland, migrated to the capital, interacted with us more closely, and expressed their superhuman sorrow—only then was it possible to grasp what even the most troubled imaginations had been unable to conceive.

And then a miraculous event occurred. In this vast misery, with the image of this bloodied, dismembered, and disgraced nation in their minds, Armenian women did not despair or distance themselves from the mourning and laments by withdrawing from active life. This is a notable point in our day and age. Living through history, that precious episode of inextinguishable national vitality may elude our admiring attention, but I am sure that future generations will reflect on it with fondness and gratitude.

Of course I do not mean to say that, after the declaration of the Constitution, Armenian women were doing large-scale and fundamental work. Remedies for almost all of the nation's problems have not yet been found, but I want to point out the psychological state that Armenian women exhibited with their general and specific efforts and their various groups organized to address both on-going needs and issues arising during moments of unexpected catastrophe. It is wrong to judge the work of any individual or group based on its lofty objectives or the twinkling quality of the organization's proposals. In any community, modest groups are the ones that carry out distinctive, enduring, and appropriate work, because they come together with absolute sincerity and are motivated only by the enthusiasm that the goal inspires. Secondly, it is because those modest groups are composed of members who are all morally invested in their work. In other words, the groups formed in this way correspond to an immediate need, while organized groups exist simply to provide a pastime for modern women, bored by their idleness, who see the purpose of activity as nothing more than a necessary detail for their image. Almost all of our benevolent societies have been brought about in this last way.

The uncompromising, stubborn hatred of the enemy should have kept our people free from class inequalities. A blow to any part of our nation is directed at the nation as a whole. Our nation was collectively disgraced by despotism, but those who were directly subjected to oppression have more of a right to hold their heads high. Considering our national circumstances as a whole, it is difficult to accept the relationship between the benefactors and recipients of their aid. Reciprocal assistance: this is the only reasonable way. Armenian women, with their pure and unadulterated instincts, felt this, and even if they did not have an absolute understanding of their direction, they felt the simplicity and tenderness of a grieving mother and weeping sister, and chose the righteous path.

Now we have before us organized women's groups both in the cities and in the villages. There is no use in naming each one individually. Whatever the political or religious banner under which they were formed, all of them are noble and loved by the nation. Daily political in-fighting will not succeed in leaving a mark on work that reflects the aspirations of the people. The day will pass and passions will fade, vain people will disappear and those who remain will be neutralized, and only a sad memory of them will remain. It is constructive work alone that will remain standing, because there is something holy in the efforts of individuals and groups with virtuous ideas. Despite everything, despite all the opposition and conspiracies, edifying work endures and advances, because it is the manifestation of the youth of the nation. It is the irrepressible, unshakable will of our tormented nation; it is our future ensured from this day on.

And to that holy work both in the provinces and in the cities, Armenian women have brought their share of devotion and vigor.

Translation by Jennifer Manoukian

Arakadz, No. 7, July 6, 1911, pp. 99-100.

NOTES

1. The reference in the title is to the 1908 restoration of the Ottoman Constitution that was designed to limit the power of the Sultan (Abdul Hamid) and increase the liberties of the people.

The Armenian Women's Role in the Current Movement towards the Homeland

When we take a quick look at the demonstrated capabilities of Armenian women and at the form of their skills and activities in the past and in this period of transition, which has been improved by today's political system, we come to the clear conclusion that their work has very many precious elements and good intentions, but that it has not yet taken its best and proper direction. This situation has caused misunderstandings, a waste of determination and efforts, and consequently, inexplicable inefficacy.

With earlier articles, I have tried to explain how Armenian women in the capital took up the task of teaching in a beautiful, voluntary movement. In the difficult, painful days of despotism, we also know how Armenian women in the provinces and their Armenian sisters in the capital, often sharing all the perils of unequal and hopeless struggles, also sometimes shared the imprisonment and exile of their husbands and brothers. And in our times, when in the terrifying days following the catastrophe it has become possible for us to grow closer to the destroyed, massacred, pitiable remnants of the Armenian nation, we have personally seen the loving relief efforts that Armenian women quickly organized and delivered from all corners, from foreign cities, Constantinople, Smyrna, and especially from other Armenian provinces.

But taking all of these encouraging signs into account, can we say that all the needs of our indigent nation have been met? Our educational work is generally as bad as it can possibly be. Even in the cities where we have the means, curricula remain in an indescribably backwards state, and there does not seem to be any drive for change, or any unease or concern among school-board members. What I mean to say is that, considering the complacency among our intellectuals, there is a good chance that the situation will continue in the same way. But this is an incomprehensible kind of neglect.

It has been three years since the doors to the homeland have been opened. Our exiles, having absorbed the advantages of civilized countries, have returned to us. Moreover, the pages of our press are free and open to express all kinds of demands and complaints, but there has been no action, not a single voice. The school years end and begin again just as they did under the old regime. Additionally, the thirst for education and enlightenment among generations in the provinces remains unquenched. Eyewitnesses talk about how, in provinces plagued by famine, the people ask for books and bread with equal fervor. Vast swathes of land inhabited by Armenians remain abandoned and unattended in complicated and crushing situations. With undying faith, the eye of the oppressed resident of the provinces turns in vain towards the good will voiced in the cities, towards public declarations by well-known individuals, and towards groups organized in their name.

It is impossible for me to describe the emotion I feel every time the most afflicted Armenian orphan girls and widows from the Adana catastrophe say the following whenever they encounter difficulty: "Write to the Armenian women. Write to the women's organizations. They understand our sorrow and will make others understand it. Why wouldn't they?" Many times these are uneducated women facing extreme misery, but each one knew by heart the names of the Armenian organizations.

And why didn't those benevolent organizations understand this sorrow or these concerns? The reason is very simple. Those organizations were founded, planned, and do their work far from the homeland, and are not in direct contact with those who benefit from it. During the old regime, an impenetrable barrier separated us from our Armenian brothers and sisters in the homeland, but what about today? I am entirely convinced that only benevolent work will move intellectual forces towards the homeland and towards the people. In the days following the declaration of the Ottoman Constitution, I dreamed of this miraculous idea. I dreamed with conviction and my belief has remained firm. One day, we will certainly witness this miracle.

From various European and American cities, Constantinople, and Smyrna, the women and girls of every social class and of every kind of ability will go to the homeland by forming delegations and dispersing themselves in the darkest, neediest corners. Some will be aristocratic Russian women, others university women or selfless girls leaving behind their bourgeois luxuries, comfortable lives, vanities, loves and passions to modestly go to the people with a newfound passion filling their souls. They will go to the suffering people in order to humbly explain why they are late, and quickly satisfy the many needs. And they will see with their own eyes, will hear with their own ears the unheard, indescribable reality of the people. On that occasion, with the inexhaustible industriousness of their female instincts, their tenderness, and their love, they will finally find the remedy for inconsolable sorrow, grief, and concern.

I am certain that the Armenians in the provinces, suddenly enlivened after the frightful oppression they faced, also dreamed of this. They waited for those delegations; they waited for the promises declared in newspapers and charters to come true. And they are still waiting. Who or which group will have the honor of being the first to achieve this miracle? How and when will this new crusade begin?

I believe in the inextinguishable vitality of our nation; I hope our national instinct, with its resilient spirit, will give birth to these women. Perhaps the day is not too far off when our girls, tired and bored of empty worldly pleasures, will plug their ears to corrupting flattery and sham courtships, close their eyes to the withering, fleeting beauty of empty appearances, and devote themselves to exciting, dynamic work for the benefit of the people.

And the scope of this work is limitless. There are children and even adults in need of instruction. There are ailing people in need of care; grieving people waiting to be consoled, and demoralized people in need of a little hope in order to be reborn. There is an entire nation, with multifaceted and complicated problems, in need of hands to reconstruct it.

And if this miracle is achieved, think of the pride that we will be able to have in answering those who considered the fate of our nation decided. Foreigners and even our own enemy elements will look on with awe at this incontestable display of our unconquerable vitality. And who knows if even one day the bursting violent, fierce passion of our enemy will not be rendered impotent by the new sweet and civilized, but rigid and stubborn form of self-defense and struggle that Armenian women have spurred.

This is the new and magnificent direction of the work that has opened up before Armenian women. The humblest as well as the most powerful and capable can be enlisted, if she is equally inspired by the mission and ready to accept the difficulty, financial hardship, danger, and serious obligation.

Translation by Jennifer Manoukian

Arakadz, No. 11, August 3, 1912, pp. 166-67.

In the Ruins

(Excerpt)

Three months after the 1909 massacre of the Armenians living in the city of Adana and its environs (in southwestern Turkey), Zabel Yessayan went to the region on a relief mission. She spent a few months working with the orphans and observing conditions there. On her return to Constantinople, she wrote a number of articles describing her experiences and, in 1911, published a book on the subject, *In the Ruins (Averagnerun mech)*. Reissued a number of times since then, in several different editions, it is one of Yessayan's most high respected and widely read works.

Under a superb, dazzling sun, the devastated city stretches outward like a boundless cemetery. Ruins everywhere . . . Nothing has been spared; all the churches, schools, and homes have been reduced to formless piles of charred stone, amongst which, here and there, the skeletons of buildings jut up. From east to west, from north to south, all the way to the distant limits of the Turkish quarters, an implacable, ferocious hatred has burned and destroyed everything. Over this deathly wasteland and these vast piles of ash, two minarets, unscathed, rise up arrogantly.

Dressed in bloody, tear-stained rags, a crowd of widows, orphans, and old people presents itself to us. This is all that is left of Adana's population. The crowd has the sullen calm of a sea stilled after a violent storm; its pain and inconsolable sorrow are hidden in its depths and sometimes rise to the surface. The hope of living, of being re-born, has been snuffed out in them. And if Hunger and Thirst had not shaken them out of their stupor, life would already have been extinguished once and for all.

They remain silent for a long time, as if following the thread of their memories, involuntarily carried along by the ghastly succession of them and breathing heartfelt sighs that seem to rip through their breasts: "*Aman*. . . ." Sometimes they break out in sobs. In a moment's time, their faces are flooded with such an abundance of gushing tears that their words of complaint and lamentation are drowned out. Then their faces, wizened and bronzed by work in the sun, are furrowed by terrible wrinkles and contorted in frightful grimaces, and the whole crowd, seized by a fit of inconsolable grief, writhes in despair. It is impossible to imagine what portion of that crowd's sorrow each particular individual represents.

Indeed, it is impossible to grasp or feel the atrocious reality all at once. It exceeds the limits of the human imagination. Even those who experienced that reality cannot describe it as a whole. All of them stammer, sigh, weep, and relate only disjointed events. The despair and terror had been so great that mothers had failed to recognize their children, and crippled, blind old people had been left behind in houses set ablaze. Listening to a savage, bloodthirsty mob's diabolical, cawing laughter, people went mad before dying. Mangled limbs and children's bodies still throbbing with life and pain were crushed underfoot. Trapped between rifles on one side and flames on the other, women, children, and the wounded who had taken refuge in churches and schools had wrapped their arms around each other, crazy with fear, as they were burned black.

Yet neither those stories, nor the dazed Armenians milling about in those ashes, nor the orphans with their grief-stricken, distracted eyes and the expressions of children still stupefied with terror on their faces, nor the bodies of the bereaved widows writhing with their inconsolable loss, nor the amputees' painful, still bleeding wounds enabled us to picture the dark enormity of what had actually happened in those hellish days. It was in people's anxious, terror-stricken eyes that sometimes, for an instant, I thought I had caught a glimpse of it. Oh, those eyes! Some looked as if they had been struck blind and forever renounced the joy of the sun; they seemed as empty as bottomless chasms. Others looked at you without seeing, because one image had been indelibly impressed on their field of vision. Some held the rhythm of the ghastly flames in their gaze; others, with pupils in perpetual motion, pupils tormented by haunting scenes of fire and blood, seemed to long for blindness and peace.

It was in that crowd that I saw the grief-stricken figure of Missak's[1] mother. Pursued by the nightmare of her son's hanging, beating her breast, tearing at her rags, she sang the praises of her martyred child and, as if thirsting for tears, kept crying, "My eyes are dried-up springs . . . my children! I have been withered by the fire in my heart . . . my children . . . *aman!*"

I saw mothers there who had strangled their babies so that their hiding place would not be betrayed by their infant cries. I saw women there who, paralyzed, their tongues lolling on their lips, were unable to cry out their heart's grief. I saw madwomen who, rather than forgetting, endlessly relived the terrible moment; I saw that they were haunted by the memory of their loved ones falling one after the other and did not know which one to mourn. . . .

"They lined them up over there, fast, one beside the next, and they fired and they fired and they fired, and all of them tottered for a moment, like this, and then toppled to the ground. It was my father and my husband and my sons, and now I'm all alone, like an owl in the ruins. Akh . . ."

Sometimes they seem indifferent, as if the intensity of their grief had turned them to stone. With calm faces on which not a muscle stirs, they recount the dreadful events. Each of their words is spilled blood. Then, suddenly, they pause, their eyes gleam with a crazy light—what image has flashed before their mind's eye?—and they shout, beside themselves, clutching at our emotion, imploring help from our tears, from our kindred feelings. . . .

In the ruined city, in their ruined hearts, all has been destroyed. I can still see the gesture of a crazed village woman: summing up everything that happened in their village with a sweeping movement of her hand, she repeated, mechanically, "If you want to believe it, believe it, if you don't want to believe it, don't; everything's over, everything's finished."

It is not the charred houses or the devastated gardens that seem past saving and past remedying in this boundless catastrophe; nor is it the large numbers of the dying. It is rather that crippling inner feeling drifting through everyone's eyes—a feeling of misery, of despondency. It is the feeling of a people that has been trampled underfoot, ground to dust under the soles of brutes. The heads that, thirsting for light and freedom, had for a moment been lifted in human dignity, have now been smashed with ruthless cruelty. Tortured by this thought, I look out at the destroyed city, whose heaps of charred rubble now take on a different and terrible meaning. And yet, amidst this deathly desolation and despair, a smile of hope blooms.

In the ruins, a group of women has taken refuge in the shade of the half-standing walls. Suspended between one wall and another, a cradle is gently rocking. Who knows? What the violence of our grief represents as impossible is perhaps possible after all for the people's untiring, unconscious genius for rebirth. For that wretched child's humble cradle, indifferent to the immense general calamity and quick with an invincible instinct for life, is rocking above this vast cemetery, disdaining both the martyred people's abject misery and the criminals' monstrous savagery. . . .

By the time we reached Mersin, I was already prepared to see a picture of the greatest desolation. Tormented by the memory of the orphans we had seen in Smyrna, my imagination was expecting similar horrors on a dreadfully larger scale. But what I saw was past all imagining. I find it hard to give an idea of the whole. Words, with their ordinary, everyday meanings, are incapable of depicting the inexpressible scene of horror that my eyes saw.

In the days when those who succeeded in escaping the flames fell victim to the rifles, when terrified, panicked people were, in their desperate efforts to save themselves, trampling invalids and the weak underfoot, most of the children had been separated from their parents and had scattered here and there. The first delegation from the Patriarchate had rounded them up a few at a time and sent them on to shelters in Mersin's Armenian school and church, so that, far from the scene of the catastrophe, the poor children might forget, to a degree, those terrible days, so that the orphans would not have to tread the ground on which their parents' blood had been spilled. Many people described the children's arrival for us. They had been nearly naked or dressed in rags that often bore traces of their mothers' blood. Their heads were bare; their eyes wandered aimlessly. They came to Mersin in groups and, in the clouds of dust raised by their bare feet, the smell of the dirt and sweat of their bodies lingered for a long time.

When they were assembled in the church, they were still terrified, and neither spoke nor cried. The fear inhabiting those little children had been so great that, when they saw anybody at all, they shivered like someone in the grip of a fever. In the imaginations of those tender innocents, grown-ups all looked the same. They saw a criminal in every adult male, were driven to distraction by atrocious likenesses, saw ghastly scenes and wanted to flee, crazed, horror-stricken, stupid with shock. Their young minds were deranged, because, for days, they had seen criminals with knives or rifles in their hands, eyes burning with a lust for evil, mouths twisted by curses and threats. Blood had spurted like rain around those children and, for hours, their pupils had been wide with the horror inspired by the flames.

Left to themselves, the boys and girls would calm down. Sometimes they conversed, although their conversations were interrupted by long silences. Sometimes all of them were carried away by the same pain; then they sobbed, refusing to be comforted, abandoned to and almost exalted by the intensity of their grief. Because their suffering exceeded their childish powers of endurance, some of them, eyes still full of tears and chests swollen with sobbing, laid their heads on their desks and slept for a long time.

Others, suddenly feeling the need for affection and familial love, fraternized with their companions in misery.

Two children had gone off by themselves and were talking.

"Do you have a father?"

"No."

"A mother?"

"No."

"I don't have a mother or father, either."

"Did they kill them?"

"Yes."

"They killed mine, too."

A long, grief-stricken silence reigned, and then:

"Do you want us to be brothers?"

And they adopted each other.

That was the general tenor of the conversations of hundreds of children between five and ten. Sometimes, too, brothers and sisters found each other again and rediscovered, in one another's eyes, the hours of terror they had spent together and did not dare come closer, as if held apart by the awful memory of the corpse of a butchered mother or father. For, almost without exception, driven by an instinctive passion for life, they wanted to forget, wanted desperately, frantically to forget; thus they saw an enemy in anyone who tried to expose the passions of their bleeding hearts, or simply stirred up the memory of that hour by his or her presence.

When I first saw those hundreds of pale, glum orphans, I was not able, my superhuman efforts notwithstanding, to grasp the whole of their misfortune; and, to this day, I still cannot. I can call details or fragmented images to mind, but I can never calculate the sum total of the infinite, bloody story represented by each particular child. I was unable to attend to them individually for a long time. It was a confused, vague, indefinable elegy that the totality of those still stunned, still stupefied, still uncomprehending young gazes expressed. That slaughter, that stream of spilled blood, the desperation of that crazed mass of humanity pinned between the flames and the daggers exceeded the limits of my understanding; and the same held, I believe, for everyone else.

These children knew that they filled me with horror. Their psychological make-up unsettled me and I could not look them in the eyes. With a sharp, irrepressible pang, I saw that there were ineradicable nightmares there, and that childhood's smile, childhood's bright, pure light had gone out in their eyes. On their dark-skinned, somber, gloomy faces, you could sometimes read, as in an open book, all the horror of hours impossible to describe; but, at other times, everything clouded over and became opaque. And that was even more disturbing.

Often they remained silent and uncommunicative when we asked them questions. Yet, when they did speak, every word gave us a glimpse of a moment of supreme agony, of a world of inextinguishable torment, grief and, above all, yearning. Some of the orphans had mothers, and every day we would witness scenes of heartrending anguish.

Occasionally, in spite of all the material difficulties involved, mothers came to Mersin, overcome in their turn by yearning. Hurriedly, anxiously, a mother would look for her own child in the group of orphans and approach it with painful nervousness; then she would stop short, as motionless as stone, not daring to kiss it. It was essential that new bonds of affection not be established between such mothers and the children who had been separated from them. These mothers instinctively understood their bitter fate, and left amid still greater sorrow and yearning.

One evening I expressed a desire to visit the children after they had gone to bed, and was ushered to their dormitory. A terrible, unforgettable sight met my eyes. In that spacious hall, on mats arranged in rows on the floor, was a welter of young, half-naked limbs. . . . Because there wasn't enough room for all of them, the children seemed to be piled up on each other. What with their breathing and all their other exhalations, the air was stifling and unbreathable. Something unnameable, something nightmarish and unsettling drifted through the semi-obscurity. The children's bodies were indistinguishable from the blackness of the sheetless beds; only the outlines of their limbs could be made out here and there, an arm, a leg. . . . Those rooms seemed as sad to me as desecrated, devastated graveyards.

Sometimes one of the children, prompted by a bad dream, would raise his head and look right and left, shuddering. One cry of his would be enough to throw all those shapeless, almost undifferentiated piles into agitated motion and, sometimes, uneasy heads would be lifted here and there. In the first few days, it sometimes happened that the ravings of one of the children rattled all the others sleeping in the same room; still half-asleep, not knowing where they were, they would all jump to their feet screaming, in the belief that they were reliving the hours of the massacre.

Although I had resolved to maintain my sangfroid, I was deeply shaken by that throng of children, deprived of affection and a mother's love and care. . . . I decided to leave so that we wouldn't disturb their sleep with our presence. Some were sighing, and all had woken up and were casting uneasy glances our way. . . .

We were getting ready to leave when I noticed a little slip of a girl almost directly at my feet. Two bright, unblinking eyes were looking at me. Her blond hair was strewn over the pillow, and her emaciated neck and emaciated arms and legs spoke of such severe mental and physical suffering that I lost control of myself, and started to cry. And, although I managed to stifle my sobs, the children heard me and woke up. For an instant, a strange stillness prevailed: they were all holding their breaths; then heads were raised, and a child started to cry. At that, as if on a signal, all at once, hundreds of children overcome by a terrifying attack of nerves suddenly began sobbing, screaming, and weeping, twisting and turning their frail, strengthless limbs on their shabby straw mats and calling out to the parents they had lost. . . .

It took us a long time to calm them down. When their tired heads at last came to rest on their pillows, the little girl's two bright eyes were still looking at me. Before leaving, when I stepped closer to see why she hadn't gone back to sleep, she stretched out a pair of arms toward my neck and held me close for a long time. . . . Before I left, I looked at all the children again. The room was quiet and peaceful. I was assured that now they would sleep soundly till morning. It seemed to me, however, that those children would dream unceasingly, with relentless insistence, of the days of horror they had lived through, and that the nightmare would hover constantly over their dark-haired heads.

Translation by G. M. Goshgarian

First published in Constantinople in 1911. Translation based on the text in Volume 1 of Zabel Yessayan's Works, *Yerger* (in Armenian), 2 vols., issued by the publishing house of the Armenian Catholicosate of Cilicia, Antelias, Lebanon, 1987, edited by Shushig Dasnabedian. English translation printed, by permission, from *Writers of Disaster: Armenian Literature in the Twentieth Century,* by Marc Nichanian (London: Gomidas Institute, 2002), pp. 316-18, 327-30.

NOTE

1. Missak was one of the Adana Armenians hanged by the Turks on the charge that they were responsible for the massacres of the Armenians [Translator's note].

Appendix

Remembering Zabel Yessayan

By Ruben Zaryan*

We had heard a great deal about Zabel Yessayan and her work, but frankly we had read none of her books. We were aware of the fact that she had lived in Paris for a long time, and that she had studied literature and philosophy at the Sorbonne. We also knew that she had lived in many other countries—Iran, Iraq, Egypt, Lebanon, Italy, Switzerland. We had also heard that in the 1920s she had come to Yerevan, and after staying here for several years she had returned to Paris, where she had written an enthusiastic book about the new Armenia and its people. We had not yet had a chance to read this book but its romantic title, *Prometheus Unbound,* intrigued us and excited our curiosity about our professor and her personality. We were further informed that in 1933 she had established herself permanently in Yerevan, where she now lived with her daughter Sophie and son Hrant.

Impatiently we now waited for her first lecture.

She arrived. No one was absent. She entered the auditorium, scanned us with a smile in her eyes, sat down, and asked us to follow suit. She begged us never again to stand up for her sake.

"I realize this request of mine may upset the present code, but it disturbs me to see you standing up. It seems such a military practice. I shall therefore ask you to express your respect toward me some other way. For example, by being punctual. You are all grown-up,

---

* Ruben Zaryan (1909-1994) graduated from Yerevan State University in 1936 and went on to a distinguished career as a writer, literary critic, and authority on the theater. This excerpt, taken from his *Memoirs* (1975), was translated from the Armenian by Ara Baliozian and first published in *Ararat* magazine (Winter 1979), pp. 10-13.

mature students who will soon enter life. I do hope, therefore, that lectures on discipline will be superfluous."

She was silent. She said nothing for a while after that. Was she reflecting on whether or not she had exhausted that particular topic? Hard to say.

She was not yet sixty at the time. Rather plump, with a serene expression on her face. Notwithstanding her age, her eyes at times were animated by fiery sparks. She had dark hair, full lips, a proud mien. At first glance she reminded one of Chloe in *Uncle Tom's Cabin,* yet there was something majestic about her appearance—her movements, her stance, her speech.

"There aren't too many of you in the audience. Is anyone absent? The entire class is present then. I shall ask you to make an effort to attend all my lectures—provided of course you are not bored. If you are bored you may feel free not to come. I have always believed that one should avoid the use of coercion in these matters, because coercion offends the soul."

Never before had we been exposed to such reasoning. We were overjoyed, but in time we came to realize that this gift of freedom bound us to her more effectively than any authoritarian regulation; and notwithstanding the sincerity of her words, I don't recall a single instance of absenteeism.

She went on to speak and we grew very fond of her. We just loved her.

"You are young: these are the best years of your life; another reason I allow you this freedom is that you may be in love and you may have arranged a date early in the day, perhaps because your girlfriend may want to see you only at that particular hour. For heaven's sake, forget the lecture and see your girl. No lecture, regardless of who is delivering it, is worth hurting her feelings."

Again she was silent. Her eyebrows bristled. Who knows what

passed through her mind. She lowered her head and when she raised it again there was a youthful smile in her eyes.

"I wasn't always old, you know. I too was young once; I too had dates to keep and my heart pounded just like yours while I waited and wondered whether he would show up; why he was so late, did he perhaps have an accident?"

Suddenly she turned to the boys of the class: "Are you as a rule punctual or late for your dates?"

"Late," replied one of the boys.

"Really?" she said, surprised.

"Of course," said some other boys.

"Shameless creatures!"

There was a motherly tone in her reproach.

"How can you say you are really in love then? Isn't impatience one of love's attributes? And you tell me you are actually capable of making the girl wait for you! I find that hard to believe. I always thought that when a young man is in love, he looks forward to his date with such furious anticipation that if he could he would move the hands of the clock forward by sheer will power."

The bell rang and our professor left us, as we remained seated silently for a moment or two. Then someone, I can't recall who, declared:

"*There's* a Professor for you!"

There was admiration as well as astonishment in this statement.

We didn't rush into the hallway as was our habit, but remained in the auditorium impatiently waiting for the bell to ring again.

In the following hour she lectured. But here too she went about it differently. She placed her chair at an angle and made herself comfortable in it. Her delivery was without pyrotechnics. Her words, though deeply felt, were spoken in an even and relaxed tone.

I remember the lectures devoted to Balzac, Flaubert, and Zola. In

Flaubert she saw a superior stylist; in Zola, psychological penetration; for Balzac, on the other hand, her admiration knew no bounds. None of her lectures impressed me as much as the one on Balzac. Some of her observations I can still remember.

"No other novelist has Balzac's all-embracing vision. *The Human Comedy* with its one hundred volumes gives the reader a more accurate description of French life in the nineteenth century than all the other works of French literature put together. The characters in it number over a thousand. Nothing is left unexplained."

On one occasion she brought with her one of Zola's books in French with a reproduction of his portrait by Monet. When we expressed some interest, she spoke of Monet, Manet, and in general of Impressionists. She felt as much at home in art as in literature. She cited dates, events, spoke of other schools, analyzed specific paintings.

Her Armenian was a charming mixture of Western and Eastern Armenian. There was an epic serenity in her delivery. Not that she was indifferent or uninvolved, though it was sometimes difficult to tell what her own preferences were—did she, for instance, think Anatole France superior to Romain Rolland?

"It is my intention to present as accurate a picture as possible of modern French literature. As a writer I may accept or reject certain trends, but as a teacher it is my duty to be historically objective."

She spoke of different literary schools, mentioning names that we had never heard before, recounting details of their activities which brought to life for us the Parisian literary scene.

After telling us all about the novels of Anatole France and Romain Rolland, and the poetry of [Guillaume] Apollinaire, she assigned each to his relative place in the panorama of French literature.

None of our professors could analyze a novel as expertly as she.

Being herself a novelist, she went out it like a craftsman—a watchmaker who took apart the mechanism of the watch and put it together again with knowing hands. In the mid-1930s she made observations on Rolland and France that three or four decades later I was to read in Russian academic works devoted to these authors.

I got and read *The Gods Are Athirst, Jean-Christophe, Colas Breugnon, The Soul Enchanted, The Fire.*[1] I read Apollinaire, Jean-Richard Bloch, [Paul] Vaillant-Couturier.

All of us without exception were under the influence of Zabel Yessayan and we thought that French literature, particularly French prose, was the best in the world.

We asked her to read for us Apollinaire's verse in the original. Though we didn't understand a word of it, we found her French seductive to the ear. We could have listened to her forever. She read with a low voice, but with intense feeling, and it seemed to us that she was deeply affected by what she read and that she relived the poet's emotional state, experiencing anew his torments and passion.

During intervals, whenever we spied an open door, we would peer in curiously to catch our professors in their unofficial capacity. Zabel Yessayan would be seated at the podium smoking. That too was a novelty for us. In those years we were not yet accustomed to seeing women smoking. But we were so much under her spell that whatever she did seemed to us correct and beautiful.

Once or twice I met her at the writers' home. On one of those occasions we even had a short talk about Mkrtich Armen's *Heghnar Fountain,* concerning which there was some controversy in the press at that time. Yessayan took part in these discussions, defending the author against his critics.

At the writers' home, someone, I can't recall who, asked Yessayan how she could suffer the inconveniences of Yerevan after the comforts of Paris. The expression on her face darkened as she delivered the following reply:

"These inconveniences are meaningless in my eyes because I take an active part in building the future of our country. Does that answer your question?"

It was 1936. There were many meetings and conferences about art and literature. The topic on that particular day was "The Struggle against Formalism and Naturalism." Drastamat Ter-Simonyan[2] was the moderator.

The conference lasted three days. Writers criticized each other and themselves. Some reputations came under fire. Bakunts's *The Walnut Trees of Brotherhood* was one of the works that was subjected to criticism. There were others who defended works of genuine literary worth. Zabel Yessayam spoke at great length and passionately about recent developments in Western European literature. I cannot exactly recall her words but I remember that part of her speech which touched on Bakunts. She stated that she saw humor as well as drama in his work. I'll never forget what she said about Charents. We were already aware of the fact that she admired Charents and was one of his loyal defenders. What she did that day, however, was more than express admiration for the poet's work in order to silence his critics; she also downgraded her own worth in order to emphasize her point. I remember well the vehemence in her voice when she declared that someday most of today's writers, including herself, would be completely forgotten, but that if they were remembered at all it would be as contemporaries of Charents.[3]

We loved our professor and we always looked forward to her lectures with great impatience. We read everything she published, as well as books—*The Gardens of Silihdar, Shirt of Fire.*

An exhibit of her late husband's (Dikran Yessayan) paintings was organized. She had been the moving spirit behind the exhibition, taking care that her husband's paintings were made available to the art-loving public. We all went to that exhibition and she was very touched by our presence.

When it became apparent that she loved the theater, one of the students asked her whether she had written any plays.

"Sure I have, but they have neither been produced nor published. I have not yet given up though. I'll try again. Maybe next time I'll be more successful."

I remember the last lecture. It was more of an informal talk, actually.

"No interruptions, please. Agreed? And with your permission I would like to smoke. All right?"

After a short pause:

"Today is a day of farewells. Perhaps we will never meet again. Probably you will soon scatter all over this big country and see each other only after a long time or never. Isn't that so?"

She took out her cigarettes and matches, placed them by her side on the desk, but didn't light one up. Her words came from the depths of her heart; they were the words of a mother who is about to be separated from her children. She spoke of our future occupations, she spoke of the responsibilities of a teacher towards his pupils; she spoke of our country and its prospects; she urged us to have faith in the future, to live and work for it regardless of whether or not we should ever live to see it. These were self-evident, simple truths, but she expressed them in such a way that they acquired a new poignancy, depth, and brilliance. I don't dare to quote her exact words because I'm afraid of distorting their unique spirit *(voki),* which was more than simply the result of experience, wisdom, and familiarity with the complexities of life.

"Before we are separated, I would like to give you the following advice: Be aware of social pressure and conditioning which tend to lead people to extremes. Be more faithful to nature. Don't think I'm now reading a Rousseauistic return-to-nature sermonette. I would just like you to be more attentive to your inner voices, closer to nature."

And here are her last words:

"If you have any problems—spiritual, emotional, financial . . . any problems at all—you can always rely on my support."

Saying this she approached Alice Manukyan, the only girl in the class, and kissed her.

"Accept this as a kiss to each and every one of you."

And she walked towards the exit, as always relaxed and serene, but with a proud bearing.

NOTES

1. French novels: *The Gods Are Athirst* by Anatole France; *Jean-Christophe, Colas Breugnon,* and *The Soul Enchanted* by Romain Rolland; and *The Fire* by Henri Barbusse.

2. Drastamat Ter-Simonyan (1895-1937) was a journalist, literary scholar, educator, and first president of the Writers' Union in Soviet Armenia.

3. Bakunts and Charents were arrested in 1936 and were victims of the Stalinist anti-intellectual purges of the times. Aksel Bakunts (1899-1937), who was especially noted for his short stories, was tried and shot to death in 1937. Yeghishe Charents (1897-1937), who died in prison from unknown causes, is today considered one of the greatest, if not the greatest, Armenian poet of the twentieth century.

Zabel Yessayan, seated at center, in Adana, Turkey, 1909, with other members of the delegation sent from Constantinople to survey conditions following the massacres of that year and to provide assistance to the Armenian orphans and refugees. *(Photo: AGBU Nubarian Library, Paris)*

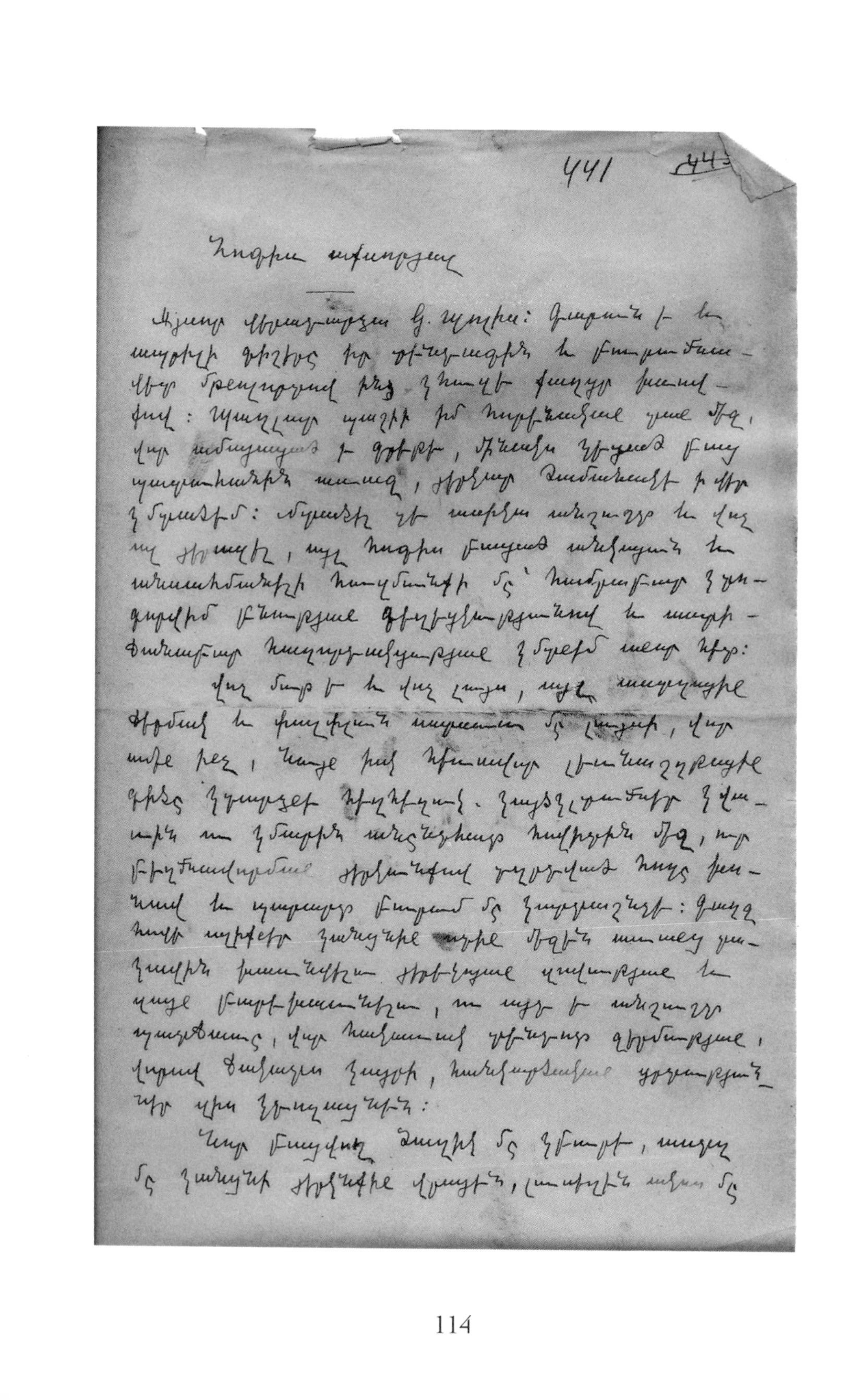

441

[illegible]

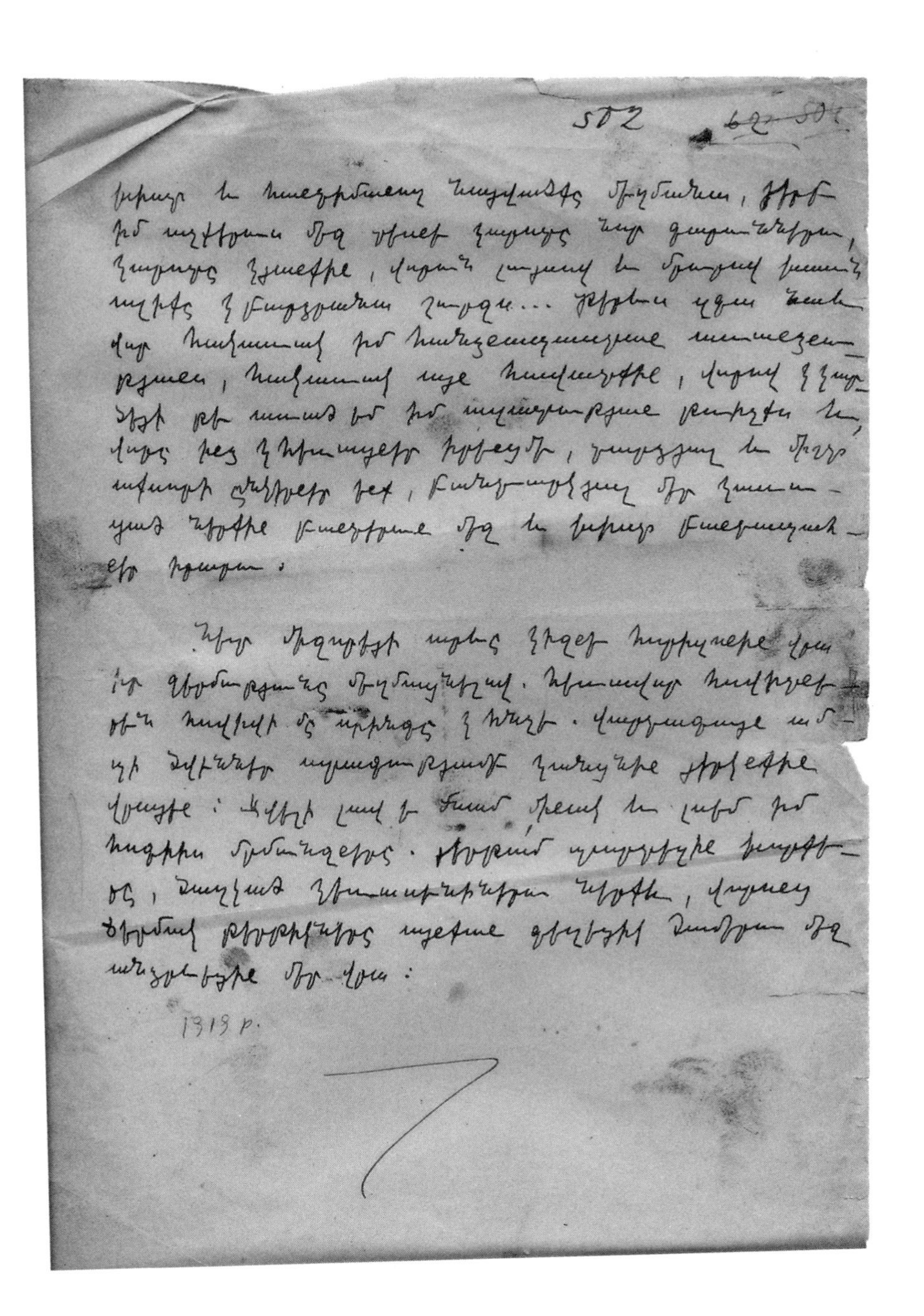

The first and last pages of the original manuscript of *My Soul in Exile*. (*Museum of Literature and Art, Yerevan, Armenia*)

Zabel Yessayan, center, in Constantinople, with several literary figures, including Krikor Zohrab, far right, and Levon Shant, between Zohrab and Yessayan.

Cover of the Armenian-language literary journal *Dzaghig* (Flower), in which several of Zabel Yessayan's earliest works were published.

English-Language Sources

By Zabel Yessayan

The Gardens of Silihdar & Other Writings, selected and translated by Ara Baliozian (New York: Ashod Press, 1982).

In the Ruins (Excerpts), in *Writers of Disaster: Armenian Literature in the Twentieth Century,* edited by Marc Nichanian (London: Gomidas Institute, 2002), pp. 315-45.

"Shirt of Fire" (Excerpt), in *The Heritage of Armenian Literature,* vol. 2, Agop J. Hacikyan, editor (Detroit: Wayne State University Press, 2006), pp. 794-98.

"The Idiot," *Gochnag,* 12 May 1917, pp. 601-2.

"Incense," *Armenian Legends and Poems,* compiled by Zabelle C.Boyajian (New York: Columbia University Press, 1959), p. 17.

"The Mother's Narration," *Lraper,* 29 June 1965, p. 4.

"The Yashmak," *Armenia,* vol. 4, no. 9 (1911), pp. 19-20.

About Zabel Yessayan

Kelikian, Hampartzoum, "Cassandra from Constantinople," *Ararat* Magazine, Autumn 1988, pp. 5-10.

Nichanian, Marc, "Zabel Yesayan: The End of Testimony and the Catastrophic Turnabout," in *Writers of Disaster: Armenian Literature in the Twentieth Century* (London: Gomidas Institute, 2002), pp. 187-242.

—"Zabel Yesayan, Woman and Witness, or the Truth of the Mask," in *New Perspectives on Turkey,* no. 41 (2010), pp. 31-53.

Rowe, Victoria, *A History of Armenian Women's Writing, 1880-1922* (London: Gomidas Institute, 2009), especially Chapter 6, "Exile and Genocide: Zabel Yesayian," pp. 217-55.

Tololyan, Khachig, "The Representation of Woman's Desire in Zabel Yesayan's Verchin Pashag'eh," in *Ararat* Magazine, Autumn 1988, pp. 80-85.

TREASURY OF ARMENIAN WOMEN'S LITERATURE

The Armenian International Women's Association publishes a series of English-language translations of works by Armenian women writers. The main focus is on the pioneering female authors who published their works in either Western or Eastern Armenian. This rich and diverse body of literature is relevant not only to present-day Armenians, but also to all those interested in multifaceted issues regarding ethnic identity, social justice, cultural values, and the evolving roles of women in society.

TITLES IN THIS SERIES

Shushan Avagian, *I Want to Live: Poems of Shushanik Kurghinian.* Bilingual edition (2005)

Diana Der-Hovanessian, *The Other Voice: Armenian Women's Poetry Through the Ages* (2005)

Zabel Yessayan, *The Gardens of Silihdar* (2014)

Zabel Yessayan, *My Soul in Exile and Other Writings* (2014)